ReNEWED CHRISTMAS BLESSINGS

A gift to:

_____

From:

_____

A Life, Repurposed Compilation

ReNEWED CHRISTMAS BLESSINGS

MICHELLE RAYBURN AND FRIENDS

FAITH CREATIVITY LIFE BOOKS

Renewed Christmas Blessings: Short Stories, Poems, and Heartfelt Essays
Copyright ©2023 Michelle Rayburn
ISBN: 978-0-9885286-9-7
Published by Faith Creativity Life Books
www.fclbooks.com

Some names have been changed to protect identities. Some stories are fictional (as labeled), and any resemblance to real people is based on a conglomeration of bits and pieces of memories combined with an overactive imagination.

Scripture quotations are taken from the Holy Bible, New Living Translation, copyright ©1996, 2004, 2015 by Tyndale House Foundation. Used by permission of Tyndale House Publishers, a Division of Tyndale House Ministries, Carol Stream, Illinois 60188. All rights reserved.

Compiled and edited by Michelle Rayburn
Cover, typesetting, and e-Book design by Michelle Rayburn
missionandmedia.com

To our readers:

The true essence of Christmas is not found in flawlessness but in the warmth of shared laughter, the comfort of cherished memories and traditions, and the beauty of renewed blessings. May this book illuminate your heart and remind you of the joy found not in perfection but in the love and grace of our Lord Jesus and his humble birth.

Contents

Festive Memories

Heart and Home

Faith and Hope

Introduction

Michelle Rayburn

O N BEHALF OF THE TWENTY-SEVEN writers who collaborated on this book, I bring you tidings of comfort and joy. Too cliché? I agree. But if there ever was a time to go overboard on anything, it has to be at Christmas. It's the holiday where too muchness reigns. Where words such as *magical, twinkling, merry,* and *glistening* are expected rather than unusual.

I knew there wasn't enough of any of that in this country girl to fill a whole volume with Christmas wonder. I'm a boy mom. This is why some of us can't have nice things. And besides, the best collections are the ones that bring multifaceted viewpoints and lessons drawn from diverse experiences. That meant I needed friends. Others to bring their perspectives and sage wisdom.

And so, from friends old and new, we invite you into this book of delightful and heartfelt true stories, charming fictional tales, and artistic poetry—an eclectic assembly of some of our happiest occasions and most difficult challenges.

In these pages, you'll find memories of family times around the table, baking sessions in the kitchen, and quiet pondering in front of the fire. You'll meet hearts yearning for home at Christmas, loved ones missing from the table, traditions from years gone by, and attitudes remodeled in the image of Jesus. You'll also find true empathy from friends who have navigated the season for the first time after losing a loved one. Precious women who have wrestled with depression or broken hearts, the sadness mingled with the true wonder and jolly laughter of this time of year.

Some are torchbearers of yuletide spirit and merriment—exuberant shoppers and party planners. God bless the extroverts who count down to December every year. Others bring a quiet, more subtle strength found in pressing on through the dark to find hope again.

Would you mind if I slipped a true confession in here? For all of my love—and I do mean LOVE—for celebrating Christmas, I have never *eagerly* skipped off to a Christmas tea. Even when I'm the keynote speaker! (Do I hear a collective gasp?) Despite how I've been blessed by the fellowship of others and how honored I am to share a word of encouragement, it isn't what energizes me most. This introvert would take a fuzzy blanket, a cozy fire, and a peppermint mocha with a handful of dear friends any day over the most charming Christmas tea. So, wherever you find yourself, welcome. Come as you are. Because we certainly did!

Through the laughter, tears, and ties of love, I know you'll discover that we're only human. What truly binds us are the ones we hold dear and the One who we celebrate. *They* make the season bright. May our stories kindle embers of your own dear memories, and may you find within these pages a reflection of hope.

Festive
Memories

The Birth of the King

Heather Norman Smith

Around the whole world there's rejoicing.
A grand chorus rings out the song.
The baby foretold is among us,
For Whom we had waited so long.
Give Him the gift of your worship.
A glad, humble heart shall you bring.
Make merry and love one another,
To honor the birth of the King.

Better Homes and Garlands

Michelle Rayburn

CHRISTMAS IS THAT TIME OF year when the scent of evergreens, ginger-bread, and peppermint fill the air. Armed with glitter and glue, we don our aprons and break out the holiday binder filled with to-do lists and spreadsheets—systems that could rival NASA's mission control. It's when women attempt to be June Cleaver and Martha Stewart all rolled into one while simultaneously creating Better Homes and Gardens worthy houses, curating fairy-tale experiences, and cultivating model children. This will inevitably include wrangling a family dressed in matching sweaters into an arrangement perfect for a Christmas photo.

> Once upon a time, I'd have been honored to be called "Michelle the Multitasking Marvel."

Once upon a time, I'd have been honored to be called "Michelle the Multitasking Marvel" for my endeavors to become a baking genius, gift-wrapping virtuoso, and decorating diva. Christmas has always held a magical appeal for me with the twinkling lights, pine garland and wreaths, marvelous fragrances, and gentle snow. Growing up with

Wisconsin winters has an uncanny way of turning a girl into a hopeless romantic. Or perhaps, a living, breathing Hallmark movie trope.

O Holy Matrimony

Our movie, which could be titled *A Spouse for Christmas*, goes something like this. Smalltown teen farm girl meets shy curly-haired boy at church. Girl eventually goes off to college in the big city, and boy considers breaking things off to let her pursue her dreams. Girl returns home to intern at local hospital. Boy and girl exchange vows a few days after Christmas at the little church where they first met. Falling snow keeps some guests from attending the wedding, but it doesn't stop boy and girl from driving three hours in a blizzard to a quaint Victorian inn for their honeymoon, arriving with girl still wearing her lace dress and hat. They lived ever after—not always happily, but always in love.

Phil and I chose Christmas for our wedding mostly because I wanted the ambiance, and I would be on break between college semesters. We were also flat broke, and a Christmas wedding would mean the church was decorated far in advance with all the magnificence of the season. I handmade some fabric and lace bows and wooden heart ornaments to include on the trees at the church and helped the decorating crew the weekend after Thanksgiving as they stapled pine boughs to plywood donuts and attached white lights to make the most gorgeous giant wreaths.

We made piles of bows from paper ribbon—remember that stuff?—attached pine boughs to form a garland along the ceiling on the platform, and poked even more boughs into sand-filled planters, filling them to overflowing with pine, baby's breath, and poinsettias. When you live rurally, a pickup load of cut pine branches costs nothing but effort.

That simple but elegant, budget-friendly celebration set the tone for the Christmases to come—at least, for a while.

Dreaming of a Magazine Christmas

In our newlywed years, I designed themed Christmas trees. In Martha Stewart style, I handmade most of my own decorations, and each year, I crafted additional ornaments to expand my coordinated collection, with hopes of achieving Better Homes and Gardens perfection.

One year, I decided to decorate the tree with homemade gingerbread cookies, so I spent an afternoon in my kitchen cutting out several batches of hearts and stars and gingerbread men. Holes poked in the tops as they came out of the oven made space to string ribbon loops through each cookie. I let them dry for a few days, and after they reached the concrete stage, they were ready to hang on the tree. I stood back to admire my work of art when finished.

Excluding the shabby tissue paper angel at the top, this was my most attractive tree yet, and the mingled smell of pine and cinnamon permeated our tiny home. I envisioned Martha nodding with approval.

Over the next few days, I had a terrible time keeping the cookie ornaments on the tree. Each morning, I found several on the floor.

"Phil, are you playing jokes on me?" I asked after a few mornings. He liked to do stuff like that to me.

"No."

"Well then, you have to stop bumping into this tree." I accused. "You keep knocking the decorations off!" Huffy me replaced the three cookies from the floor.

"It isn't me," he defended. "Maybe your cookies are too heavy."

"Whatever."

One morning, as I looped the string back on a branch, I noticed that one of the cookies had been embossed with a little fringe of scratching around the edges.

"Honey, what is this?" I asked.

"Looks like teeth marks."

"Teeth marks!" I dropped the cookie as if it had burned me. Martha never warned of this prospect.

"Well, I've possibly seen something dark and furry run into the register a few times."

When Phil says he possibly saw something, it means he *did* see something. He likes to break bad news gently. I shivered at the thought of a greedy mouse climbing around in my tree, sliding down the branches, and riding a cookie to the floor. The audacity! While. I. Was. Sleeping.

"Set a trap. Puh-leeeeze!"

It's Beginning to Look a Lot Like "Kitschy"

Christmas perfection took a back seat when my two boys were old enough to help decorate the tree. We went for the clumpy effect. Wherever they could reach, they clustered a bunch of ornaments. And it took things to a new level when they started bringing home "artistic" pieces to add to our ornament collection.

They made oodles of creative things at Sunday school, those Oriental Trading Company pieces that have a spot for a child's photo in the middle of the foam snowman assemblage. Many have school pictures of my children at various ages, and most are fashioned from construction paper, popsicle sticks, wobbly eyes, glitter, sequins, fuzzy pipe cleaners, and excessive amounts of dried glue. Ornaments the size of paper plates. Marshmallow snowmen. Handprints.

These treasures are the inspired art projects of teachers who, no doubt, wanted to ensure that I'd have boxes of goodies to pass off to my children when they left home someday. Perhaps those teachers knew that someday I'd shed a tear every time I put that one-eyed toilet paper roll reindeer on the tree when an empty nest meant decorating the branches alone. Gone are the popcorn strings—the mice liked those too—and vanished are the construction paper chains.

Michelle the Multitasking Marvel has also left the building. In her place, a new model. Michelle the Minimalist Maven. This 2.0 version of the bride of thirty-something years ago knows that even Santa had a team of reindeer to help him out. She favors fuzzy slippers, peppermint mocha, and vanilla wood-wick candles that crackle.

This version knows the real magic of Christmas lies in the laughter, love, and the occasional wonky-looking gingerbread house. She knows that being gloriously imperfect is great news because the Light of the World invites us to become people who reflect his perfect light.

> Michelle the Multitasking Marvel has also left the building. In her place, a new model. Michelle the Minimalist Maven.

All I Want for Christmas Is Hope

While I bask in Jesus's magnificent grace, he renews something in me: hope. One of my favorite verses is Isaiah 61:3. As a fan of all things re-purposing, it reminds me that the biggest renewal of all happened when Jesus came into the world. "To all who mourn in Israel, he will give a crown of beauty for ashes, a joyous blessing instead of mourning, festive praise instead of despair."

The ashes—a symbol throughout the Bible of mourning—were placed on foreheads after removing their head covering. Some translations of that verse speak of the crown of beauty as a garland, a symbol of glory put back in place as a head covering. Jesus came to restore. To bring his people better homes and garlands. Well, actually, better *hopes* and garlands.

He would later quote the same passage, saying he came to bring good news, to "proclaim that captives will be released, that the blind will see, that the oppressed will be set free" (Luke 4:18). What he did for Israel, he does for me too. He restores. He releases the oppression of whatever binds me.

As the glitter settles and the scent of cookies lingers, I pause to remember that amid traditions and memories, perfection was never the goal. Christmas is and will always be a celebration of hope and grace. So, I embrace the season with an open heart—and without an agenda. The miracle isn't in how much I can do. It's in how much he can remake me to become like him.

Christmas Portal

Becky Melby

ALL I WANT FOR CHRISTMAS is peace and quiet!"

I shot the words at my husband, then stopped at the base of the stairs, listening to the silence. "No. Not quiet. All I want for Christmas is a time machine. I want Christmas like it was when we were kids. No. Like when my parents were kids. I want simple and . . . un-plugged. I want connection." I closed my eyes against the press of tears. "I want talking. Real conversations with the man I married and the people I gave birth to."

I ascended the stairs to a hallway lined with doors that had simul-taneously shut when we returned home from the candlelight service at church. Anything-but-Christmasy music slithered under the door on my left. "Yeah! He scores!" came from the one on the right. Virtual re-ality basketball. I leaned my forehead on the next door, listening to the muffled dialogue of my youngest's favorite show.

Yes, we'd said they could have more screen time during vacation, but I'd envisioned some of it shared. "Who wants to watch *It's a Wonderful Life?*" I'd asked on the way home from church. A chorus of groans fol-lowed by a trio of excuses had answered my question.

The door at the end of the hall slammed. Behind me. I flopped onto the bed, face down, and sobbed and ranted into my pillow. I'd spent the past week shopping, wrapping, baking, and cleaning, motivated by a pie-in-the-sky fantasy of a postcard Christmas. Did they even know? Would they care if they did? Who was I doing this for? I'd thought it was for them, but maybe it was only for show, for some fake, posed social media shots to impress . . . who?

Tomorrow, before my parents arrived, I'd take away their devices. "Three hours. You can survive three hours without them," I'd say. There would be pouting. And whining. And probably attempts to hide phones under the table during Christmas dinner. And then, when the sink was full of dirty dishes and the living room floor covered in torn paper and tangles of ribbon, the doors would close again.

I swiped at my face. I was over-tired, over-extended, and a bit hormonal. All I needed was a good night's sleep. And a lot of chocolate. I sat up and opened my nightstand drawer and pulled out a half-empty bag of Dove dark chocolate "gifts"—the ones that hadn't found their way into the stockings I'd hung by the chimney with care. Shiny red squares with gold bows on the wrappers. I opened one, took a deep breath, and plopped the glossy chocolate onto my tongue. My endorphins applauded. My shoulders lowered. I smoothed out the wrapper on my knee and read the words.

DO YOU.

I laughed. Like anyone would say that to a mother of three. I opened another one.

MAKE THE CALL.

To whom? I could call my sister. Or Jen, my neighbor. But what was the point? We were all living mirror lives. Just one more . . .

BOOK THE FLIGHT.

Now we're talking. Christmas in Tahiti. Lounge chair, umbrella drink, uninterrupted reading. Alone.

LIVE YOUR LIFE EVERY DAY WITH NO REGRETS. IT'LL BE WORTH IT.

Hmm. Good words. If I left or went ballistic on the people under my roof, I'd always look back on this as the Christmas to forget.

EVERYTHING WILL BE OKAY IN THE END. IF IT'S NOT OKAY, IT'S NOT THE END.

Two more, and then I leaned back on a pile of pillows. As exhaustion overcame the sugar rush, I closed my eyes. *No regrets. I can do this. It's not over yet. Tomorrow will be better. I will make it better. It's not the end. Everything will be o . . .*

I WOKE LATER THAN USUAL on Christmas morning to puffy eyes and a damp pillow. The sky outside my window was dark and heavy, much like my mood. But maybe they were snow-filled clouds. Snow would help.

I heard footsteps—Middle Child, shadowboxing in pajamas and VR headset—followed by chatter and laughter. My "baby." At seven, she should have been jumping on our bed before the sun came up, begging to open that one present we'd give them before Grandma and Grandpa arrived. Instead, I knew she was in her own bed watching *Fuller House* reruns. My oldest would still be sleeping. And the man I hadn't heard come to bed last night or get up this morning would be sipping coffee, eyes glued to a screen.

"I can't do this." As the feeble chocolate-fueled optimism I'd manufactured last night evaporated, I whispered the words to the ceiling fan. I swung my legs over the side of the bed. My toes kicked something that made a soft tinkling sound. "Gift" wrappers. A spike of thin light lasered through the blinds and landed on the silvery square next to my big toe. *YOUR VIBE ATTRACTS YOUR TRIBE.*

It wasn't the first time God had used a dove to convey a message. Was my PMS-driven vibe contributing to the silence? Repelling instead of attracting?

LIVE YOUR LIFE EVERY DAY WITHOUT REGRET. IT WILL BE WORTH IT.

But how? My vibe might be beyond changing, and I already had more regrets than Dove had slogans.

I slogged into the bathroom. A wrapped box with an envelope attached sat on the counter. I opened the envelope and pulled out a card with a hand-drawn picture on the front. A bathtub overflowing with bubbles. My vision blurred as I read the words inside.

MERRY CHRISTMAS, MOM. WE
APPRECIATE ALL YOU DO FOR US.

BREAKFAST WILL BE READY AT NINE.
RELAX UNTIL THEN. LOVE YOU.

It was signed by all four of the people I'd ranted about last night.

Was I dreaming?

I opened the box. Three red-striped, peppermint-scented candles, a box of matches, and a bottle of bubble bath.

Tears dripping off my chin, I turned on the water, shed my pajamas, and slid under a blanket of shimmering bubbles reflecting candlelight.

At nine o'clock, dressed and wearing a sheepish smile, I walked down the stairs.

A sign hung above the dining room doorway.

24-HOUR CHRISTMAS TIME PORTAL

The chatter I'd heard came from the kitchen, where all four of my people stood around the island chopping, stirring, and buttering, and from the TV, where Jimmy Stewart ran through the snow in a black-and-white Bedford Falls.

A chorus of "Merry Christmas, Mom!" greeted me. Middle Child pulled out a chair. I gaped at him in dress shirt and black pants. Damp hair combed. My oldest set a plate of warm, frosted cinnamon rolls on the table set with a red tablecloth and the good china, while my youngest, curls bouncing, walked slowly toward me with a glass of orange juice. My girls were wearing dresses. The man I'd yelled at last night placed a platter of bacon and a bowl of scrambled eggs on the table and a lingering kiss on my lips, then held out his hand. "Phone, please."

I laughed as I reached into my sweater pocket, handed over my phone, then watched him slip it into a box decorated like an Old West jail. Laughter turned to tears as my people sat and reached out to me. We held hands as my husband prayed a blessing over food I hadn't cooked. When I looked up, blinking through yet more tears, words wouldn't come. "H-how?" I stammered.

"Time portal." Middle Child stabbed a forkful of eggs. "After we clean the kitchen and put the turkey in the oven and open one present, we're going to sing Christmas carols."

"And then play Scrabble. Unless you'd rather read." The sixteen-year-old smiled. And made eye contact.

I pinched my elbow. It hurt. I was awake, and this was real. Temporary, but real. "Scrabble would be perfect." I looked at the man who maybe hadn't come to bed at all last night. "Why?"

"Because I would lasso the moon for you, Mary. Or build you a time machine if that's what you want."

"Look!" Curls bobbing, my youngest pointed at the window, where huge flakes drifted straight down from a pewter sky.

Tomorrow would come. Reality would return, and doors would close. But for now, I would live this wonderful life without regrets.

Buffy and Biff

Kelly Wilson Mize

S IT TIME YET, GRANDMOTHER?" I pestered, even though there was not even the slightest sliver of daylight yet illuminating the dark room.

"Not yet, honey," she sighed wearily. I found comfort in her familiar scent of wrinkle cream and antacids—a combination that, for me, always represented security and unconditional love.

It was early Christmas morning, around 1975. I was about five years old and sharing a bed, as I often did, with my grandmother. Not long after the lights were turned out on Christmas Eve, my interrogation had begun. "What time is it now? What time can we get up in the morning? Do you think Santa will share the cookies with Rudolph?" I chattered on and on. Eventually, I could tell that her patience with me was starting to wane, but she remained kind in her responses.

My paternal grandmother was the only grandparent I had ever known. She was my part-time caretaker, friend, and playmate. Opal Wilson had been a dearly loved third-grade teacher for decades. I have heard the words, "Mrs. Wilson was my favorite teacher!" countless times from former students throughout my life. But I was the most fortunate recipient of her guidance because when I was very young, she retired from the classroom and came to live with my parents and me.

Grandmother had given up her role in education to help my parents, who were knee-deep in ministry. She cooked, cleaned, organized, and tended a garden. But most of all, she took care of me, her youngest grandchild. Like countless children before me, "Mrs. Wilson" would quickly become *my* favorite teacher too. She taught me to read, to swim, and to do long division. She prepared an afternoon snack for me every day and made costumes for many school performances. Grandmother taught me the definition of sacrificial love—what it meant to put others first. Even as a small child, she made me feel as though I was her highest priority. But not just me. She pretty much made everyone feel that way.

I have one sibling, a brother named Phil, who is fourteen years older than me. Because of the huge age difference, it's hard for me to remember a time we even lived in the same house. But Phil was not my only brother. Tragically, my parents lost a three-year-old son named Paul in a horrible accident before I was born. Paul had always been a beloved subject of conversation in my family, and I so desperately wanted to know the brother I had never known. I often wondered (and still do!): Would we have been friends? Would we have argued?

Since Paul was closer to my age than Phil, I often dreamed of what it would have been like to have Paul be a part of my life growing up. But of course, he never would be. Instead, my grandmother was my primary playmate and my first best friend. Her presence helped fill a void in all of our hearts.

On that Christmas Eve, Grandmother told me a bedtime story, as was our daily tradition. The story starred my two favorite characters, Buffy and Biff. As far as I know, their names were original products of my grandmother's creativity. And oh, Buffy and Biff were two of a kind!

I was so fascinated by how, in every story, Buffy and Biff seemed to take part in precisely the same activities that my Grandmother and I had that day. If we had gone for a walk, Buffy and Biff did too. If we had crafted paper flowers, so did Buffy and Biff. If I had helped my grandmother pick blackberries and bake a cobbler that day, Buffy and Biff did the exact same thing!

I looked forward to hearing the beloved bedtime stories that recapped the highlights of our days. I was never quite sure which one of us was Buffy and which was Biff. But I did know one thing–*they* were *us*. We were a team. As I listened attentively to the stories my grandmother told, I sometimes wondered if she had once told my brothers Phil and Paul stories about Buffy and Biff too.

> Buffy and Biff seemed to take part in precisely the same activities that my Grandmother and I had that day.

On that particular Christmas Eve night, Buffy and Biff were, of course, eager for Christmas morning and waiting on Santa just like we were. They discussed the true meaning of Christmas—the baby Jesus, born to Mary and Joseph and placed in a manger. Buffy and Biff tried to guess the gifts that were wrapped under the tree and waiting to be opened the following day, and they looked forward to the traditional feast that would bring the family together around the table for Christmas dinner.

What seemed more like days than hours after that Christmas Eve story, the sun began to slowly peek through the thin curtains in the bedroom we shared. The excruciating suspense I experienced waiting for Christmas Day was almost over.

But regardless of all that anticipation, I don't even remember what my presents were that year. I'm sure they were magical offerings similar to other childhood Christmases: a stocking filled with treats, maybe a doll, a book—the number of gifts always delightfully abundant.

What I do remember, though, is the precious time that was spent with my grandmother as we awaited Christmas. Her presence and patient spirit always provided security and an assurance that everything would, indeed, be just as it should be. And her attention was not given only on "special" days but every day. That Christmas, amid all the excitement of presents, I learned the value of *presence*. And just as my Grandmother was with me whenever I needed her, she taught me about another who would always be with me, the One who would provide love and guidance, no matter how old I grew or how far away I roamed.

That baby in the manger that Buffy and Biff spoke of was born for a very important reason—to save the world and to save *me*. He would never leave me or forsake me. When I am in need of a renewed sense of God's presence, I recall the concept that my grandmother so beautifully illustrated.

Grandmother died when my children were toddlers, and even though they don't really remember her, I'm so glad she was able to meet them. As they were growing up, they were told countless tales about their great-grandmother. But for some reason, the bedtime stories I told them never included the antics of Buffy and Biff. Maybe those characters were sacred, a special tradition meant to be shared only between my grandmother and me. Even so, I hope to one day have the opportunity to carry on her legacy and create special traditions (and bedtime story characters) with my own grandchildren.

> I hope to one day have the opportunity to carry on her legacy and create special traditions.

Since her death more than twenty years ago, I have found great comfort in knowing that my grandmother and my brother Paul are now together in heaven. I imagine them reading and playing and telling stories in the presence of Jesus himself. I hope they are able to look down and see the good things that happen in my life and the lives of our family members—and that they each know how much I love them. I can't wait to see my grandmother again one day and finally meet my brother for the very first time. When I do, I have a vast collection of Buffy and Biff stories to tell them both.

The Christmas Kitchen

Mel Tavares

CHRISTMAS AND KITCHEN CREATIONS HAVE been synonymous in our family for generations. We carve out two weeks annually to create a variety of delectable treats and then assemble them onto a platter to hand out to neighbors, family, and friends as gifts. Over the centuries, recipes have been handed down, and the methods taught to children as young as two and three.

Ambiance is essential to the outcome of the baking process, or so I have always believed. A playlist of classic carols is a must. Without fail, every year, the lyrics to "Blue Christmas" bring on tears. We sing along as we insert names of the loved ones no longer with us, the career-minded kid who has moved away to pursue an opportunity and cannot make the trip to be home for Christmas, as well as those who are now shut-ins. I digress.

Christmas lights are necessary to set the ambiance, and if there's been time to decorate the tree before the annual bake-a-thon, all the better to set the stage for the scene straight out of the Betty Crocker Test Kitchens.

Hand-crafted chocolates play center stage on the platters of scrumptious sweets. In a time when factories churn out boxes of chocolates and store-front candy shops offer a plethora of choices, it might seem a waste of time to continue the aged tradition of forming and dipping each chocolate. Yet the recipients know the love and care shown by our family, who take the time to be part-time chocolatiers.

Ingredient choices are important when doing any cooking, baking, and candy-making. I recall my mum telling us very specific brands that must be used. I learned the hard way to stick to tested methods rather than cut corners in the kitchen. As a young teen, I didn't understand the logic, and as a young adult, I opted to change brands used for decades by the older generation. It turns out mother does know best. So does grandmother and great-grandmother!

> learned the hard way to stick to tested methods rather than cut corners in the kitchen.

More than once, I tried to substitute with lower-cost ingredients and have had to throw a batch out because the lower cost also meant a lower quality. Cheap peanut butter and graham crackers, for example, result in an entirely different-tasting peanut butter ball. Using imitation flavorings rather than the more expensive flavoring oils produces bland-tasting chocolate creams. I now understand the brand and mixture of chocolate is as important as maintaining a low heat while dipping and that not all brands melt enough to eliminate lumps and create a smooth finish on the time-consuming trays of chocolates.

We've always made the chocolates at the beginning of our bake-a-thon, as they have a longer shelf-life than baked goods. Next comes the making of the cookies. Liberally frosted and decorated Christmas cookies have adorned the assembled trays each year for as far back as I can remember. Our family recipe box is filled with grease-stained cookie recipes, with a section dedicated to holiday traditions. Must-make recipes include sugar, oatmeal-raisin, snickerdoodles, and soft date-filled molasses cookies.

I've added a few of my own favorites to the traditions I am passing down through my children and grandchildren. As an adult, I discovered the joy of making and personalizing gingerbread men and women, similar to what I had seen in my beloved childhood book *The Gingerbread Man*. The researcher in me discovered the tradition of personalizing cookies dates back to at least the fifteenth century when the Roman Emperor Fredrick III distributed molded cookies in his likeness.[1] The English colonists brought the tradition to America, but it was not until 1875, when the book was released, that baking gingerbread men gained popularity. Every year, I quote the 1875 classic story as the family gathers on cookie-decorating night and laugh as the younger kids begin play-acting with their gingerbread people.

The COVID-19 pandemic nearly destroyed our decades-old tradition of the cookie-decorating night in the "Christmas Kitchen" until I realized that we could do things differently. (Didn't we all learn to do everything differently during those pandemic years?) I baked hundreds of gingerbread and sugar cookies, ordered dozens of tubes of frosting and a variety of decorative candies online, and purchased containers to create personalized kits. Once the individual kits were assembled, we made deliveries to the in-state kids and sent shipments to the out-of-state households.

It is hard to put into words the joy I felt as each received their kits and sat with their households to decorate the cookies I had baked—they video-chatted with me or texted photos of their evening. While I missed the comradery of being gathered at our long farmhouse table, there was satisfaction in knowing all was not lost, and the time would soon come when we could be together again.

Our Christmas Kitchen sessions also include making something called "Doo-Dads." That's the nickname of the snack mix our family slow-bakes in the oven, cools, and bags before placing it in a prominent position on the holiday gift trays. I'm fairly certain the recipe originated in a magazine somewhere as a homemade version of Chex party mix (see our recipe at the end of this chapter). Making this has always been one of the tasks delegated to younger kids because of the ease of measuring and mixing the dry ingredients. We use a ten or fifteen-quart mixing bowl because of the batch size. I recall as a child feeling somewhat slighted by being told I was not old enough to evenly drizzle the melted butter and Worcestershire over the mix, which had been transferred into roasting pans, but I now find myself metering out the task only to the teens and adults—for the same reasons.

Baked-from-scratch quick breads have always been a part of the Christmas Kitchen gifts from our family as well. I have yet to figure out the importance of only mixing and baking one batch at a time in a specific order, but my mum insisted this was the way it needed to be done. So, for the many years I baked with her, we did it her way.

First, we made the pumpkin bread. Next, the banana bread, and then the zucchini bread. While those were being timed to perfection, we chopped dates for date bread and cherries to go into the cherry-nut bread. As each pan came out of the oven and we turned the breads onto the cooling rack, we were reminded to thoroughly wash the pans and start afresh with the next batch. Once cooled, each loaf was tightly sealed in plastic wrap and then strategically placed around the edges of the platter. I confess that since my mum passed away, I have not adhered to her structured order of making the breads.

> I feel the joy and anticipation as we approach a home and bring the Christmas gift from the kitchen,

Usually bleary-eyed from pulling near all-nighters in the final days of the bake-a-thon, the remaining die-hard bakers wrap each platter in layers of plastic wrap to prevent air from destroying the hours of labor. No platter would be complete without a hand-written Christmas card and bow added to the top. Then we transport platters to delivery vehicles. Each year, I feel the joy and anticipation as we approach a home and bring the Christmas gift from the kitchen, knowing the friend or neighbor will savor each of the sweet treats adorning the platter.

The Christmas Kitchen is open to whosoever will in the family. Not all family members stay for the entire bake-a-thon. Some come for the candy making. Others come for the cookie making. Most engage in cookie decorating. There are always a few who come for the eggnog and pizza, vowing never to bake and only to eat the kitchen treats. Memories are shared and made, stories and laughter abound, and bellies are filled.

Many things have changed in the world around us, and families seem busier than ever. Still, I remain committed to the time-honored tradition of holiday baking, doing my part to ensure the legacy of the Christmas Kitchen continues long after I go to my heavenly home.

Doo-Dads Recipe

Mel Tavares

Oven temperature: 250 degrees

You will need a large (10–15 quart) mixing bowl and large baking sheets or roasting pans.

1. Mix together and set aside:

> 1 3/4 cups of melted butter
> 1/3 cup of Worcestershire sauce
> 1 teaspoon garlic powder

2. Add the following dry ingredients to a large bowl and mix together:

> 3 cups of peanuts
> 3 cups of pretzel sticks
> 4 cups of Cheez-It crackers
> 2 cups of Cheerios cereal
> 3 1/3 cups Corn Chex cereal
> 3 1/3 cups Rice Chex cereal
> 3 1/3 cups Wheat Chex cereal

3. Pour the melted butter/Worcestershire sauce mixture over the dry ingredients until thoroughly coated. Note: I divide dry ingredients into roasting pans and then pour the butter mixture over and mix, but mixing in a bowl works well, especially if you will use baking sheets in the oven.

4. Place in pre-heated 250-degree oven and cook 15 minutes. Stir. Repeat 3 times for a total cooking time of 45 minutes.

5. Dump baked Doo-Dads onto paper towels and let sit until they harden. Store in an airtight container or zipper bags.

Snapshots of Christmas Past

Joanie Shawhan

MY NINETY-FOUR-YEAR-OLD MOM PICKED UP a handful of old photographs from one of the boxes strewn across the dining room table at our family reunion. "I want you kids to go through all these pictures and take the ones you want."

One by one, I shuffled through a stack of glossy prints. Every picture told a story—a precious memory captured in still life.

Snapshots of Family Christmases

"Is this you?" My brother interrupted my musings and handed me a colorized photo. A five-year-old in a red corduroy jumper sat on the floor in front of a box almost as big as she, staring at a shiny copper tea set. Our Charlie Brown Christmas tree stood in the middle of the playpen, protected from my then-toddler brother.

My brother chuckled as he handed me another Christmas photo. I peered at the wide grin revealing two new front teeth and my beaming face framed by home-permed hair. I could barely cradle the twenty-four-inch doll in my arms.

The photo transported me back to that Christmas. On Christmas Eve, we'd heard a knock at the door. We looked at one another, and someone said, "Who could that be?"

My dad slipped into the living room. "Why don't you check it out?"

A chilly wind greeted us as we opened the door. But no one was there. In the glow of the porch light sat a huge box overflowing with colorfully wrapped presents. Our voices chimed in unison: "Santa came! Did you see him?" "Why did he leave our presents on the porch?" "Can we open them tonight?"

My dad laughed as he hefted the box inside and arranged the gifts under the tree. "Well, Santa knew we didn't have a chimney, so where else would he leave your presents?" For the first time, we opened our gifts on Christmas Eve.

I believe that was the year we were introduced to the Sears Roebuck and Co. Wish Book Catalog. I remember clutching the toy catalog in my hand. My fingers carefully opened each glossy page filled with color photos of the newest toys. I drooled over the dolls dressed in pink with their pink layettes and their very own cribs. I turned page after page until I found the dollhouses accessorized with tiny furniture designed for their miniature families.

"Mom, do you have a pencil? I want to circle everything I want for Christmas."

"You can mark what you want, but there's only so much money to go around for all of you."

> We could hardly wait for the Christmas Wish Book to show up at our door.

Before my brothers found the catalog, I grabbed a pencil and marked my top picks. Thereafter, we could hardly wait for the Christmas Wish Book to show up at our door.

What a fun memory.

I flipped through another handful of photos and found another picture of me in a red dress, seated next to a white-flocked tree. By this time, my taste in dolls had graduated. I held up a Barbie in a striped canopy swing. She needed a fashionable wardrobe, but Barbie clothes were expensive.

I recalled opening another present. The package contained tailored outfits for my Barbie: a blue-paisley fringed skirt and top with tiny snaps and a fully lined dark green wool skirt and jacket. Each ensemble included a matching lined hat created with the medicine cups my mom saved from her recent maternity hospitalization. The cups were just the right size for Barbie's head.

After a long day of caring for us kids and the house, my mom had sat down at her sewing machine and sewed Barbie clothes for me from the scraps of fabric and notions she collected.

Snapshots of Christmas Parties

I sorted through more photos until I landed upon a black-and-white photo of our family with aunts, uncles, and cousins clustered around a Christmas tree. Each year, we had gathered with my mom's family for a Christmas dinner and a gift exchange. When our extended family outgrew individual homes, we met in a church hall or school.

Every year at Christmas, my grandpa made a special trip to the bank. He withdrew fifty dollars in new one-dollar bills and placed each one in an envelope. One by one, he called the names of his grandchildren and gave each of us an envelope containing one dollar. That was a lot of money for us.

One year, my grandma arrived at the party with a stack of packages wrapped with brown paper and tied with a string. Each of her nine children drew a number and received the corresponding package. We swarmed around my mom as she opened her gift. She unfurled a quilted bedspread adorned with butterflies. My grandma had handsewn each butterfly onto a white square bordered by strips of turquoise. She had used scraps of material from her house dresses and aprons to create each hand-quilted bedspread on her quilting loom.

One of my dad's co-workers at the local television studio must have snapped the next black-and-white photo. The six of us stood between long rows of tables covered with white tablecloths at my dad's work

Christmas party. Even though I was a big girl of ten and didn't believe in Santa anymore, I hoped my name was tagged on one of the colorful packages piled high around the brightly lit tree.

After dinner, Saint Nick arrived with a "Ho, ho, ho! Merry Christmas!" One by one, he reached for a package and called a child's name. I watched the pile shrink. Finally, he called my name. I wrapped my arms around the oversized box, raced back to the table, and tore off the wrapping. A cotton candy machine! I couldn't wait to swirl the fluffy pink and blue sugar around the paper tubes.

Snapshots of Christmas Traditions

As our family grew to a final count of nine, the number of Christmas photos dwindled, but not the memories.

Eventually we moved into a larger home that included a fireplace. Store-bought stockings for all of us would be too expensive, so my mom took on another late-night project. She cut and sewed each of us a red felt Christmas stocking with a white top. On the stockings, she wrote our names in cursive with gold glitter.

On Christmas morning, we bounded down the stairs and raced over to the fireplace. "Look, we have stockings!" I felt around my stocking and discovered a bulge in the toe. I pulled out the biggest orange I had ever seen. But there was still a lump. Again, I worked my fingers around the inside of the stocking and pulled out a large Red Delicious apple. I had only seen fruit that size in a store. Each Christmas after that, a large orange and apple found their way into each of our stockings. I relished every bite.

One year, my mom gathered us around the dining room table and gave us a new project. We created homemade Christmas ornaments. We folded and refolded colorful foil paper and then cut slivers and shapes along the folds. As I unfolded my paper, I marveled at the unique design cut into the ornament, shiny and ready to hang. We also made ornaments from Styrofoam balls with ribbon, sequins, and beads left over from other projects.

Another year, just before Christmas, my mom pulled a heavy wooden box out of the buffet cabinet and set it on the dining room table.

"Mom, why do you have the good silverware out?" I wasn't aware of any fancy dinners that warranted her sterling silver.

"I'm going to sell it. We don't really use it anymore."

"But mom, that's your wedding silver."

Many years later, I learned that her wedding silver had paid for Christmas presents that year when my dad was out of work.

Snapshots of Christmas Customs

As a family, we celebrated Advent. Before dinner, we gathered around our walnut dining room table, lit the appropriate candles in the Advent wreath, and prayed. Each Sunday, we lit an additional candle until the flames flickered on all four candles: hope, peace, joy, and love. While the candles illuminated our darkened dining room, we filed into the kitchen for supper.

> Each Sunday, we lit an additional candle until the flames flickered on all four candles: hope, peace, joy, and love.

One evening during dinner, we smelled something burning. It wasn't our supper. Smoke wafted around the corner into the kitchen. Crackling flames shot up from the table. I froze. My mom grabbed a throw rug and smothered the flames.

I stared at the charred wood in the center of the table and the smoke-blackened ceiling. A lighted Advent candle had tipped over and started the blaze. I shivered, though not from the cold. Our turn-of-the-century home could have gone up in flames. I grieved as I ran my fingers over the rough, blackened wood.

My parents scrubbed the soot off the ceiling, but could our vintage table be repaired? One day, I came home from school and surveyed the empty space once graced by our table. Several weeks later, the professionals returned our table, restored like new. All traces of the fire faded into a distant memory. But we never again left the lit Advent candles unattended.

AS MY SIBLINGS AND I looked through the snapshots of past Christmases and shared memories, I felt grateful for the times we spent together as a family. We never received all the toys we circled in the Sears Wish Book, but by Christmas morning, it never mattered. We were thrilled with our gifts: one major toy we wanted, a robe or pajamas, socks, and a game we could share.

Even with a tight budget, my parents scrimped, saved, and sacrificed so we could always have Christmas.

Purple Patty

Kathy Carlton Willis

O N TIPPY-TOES, I PICKED UP the handset of the black, rotary-dial wall phone. Dialing just five numbers, I reached my best friend, next-door neighbor Patty Rubemeyer. "Hi, Patty! What did Santa bring you this Christmas?"[2]

"He brought me a doll bed, and a teddy bear, and a . . . and a . . ."

Every year, we called each other when gift opening was complete. On Christmas Day, we never walked across the alley to talk because chatting over the phone like grown-ups was half the fun. Often our parents compared Christmas lists when deciding what Santa should bring. One year, Patty received the walking version of a doll, and I received the talking version. We believed they were twins!

The Christmas after I turned six, we both found sewing kits under our trees. Not knowing what a needle threader was, I threw away what I believed to be the *label*. Later, Mrs. Rubemeyer kidded me about my "poochy" lip when I pouted about the missing threader. I wanted my sewing kit to be just like Patty's!

Patty and I did everything together. We walked to school together. We played together. And when called for, we were even disciplined together. It was not unusual to see Patty's nose pointed in one corner of the room and mine in another as our mothers grew impatient with our antics.

The neighborhood kids formed a close-knit family. Each home an extension of our own. The Rubemeyers all played a vital role in shaping my life. Patty taught me many lessons. She told me the secret of Santa and the facts of life. There wasn't much we didn't share. Even after we no longer believed in Santa, Patty and I called every Christmas of our childhood to talk about our gifts.

The Gift of a New Name

Phone calls changed as we approached adolescence. We chatted about friends and activities. Our porch swings became a favorite hangout spot. When excited, legs pumped the swing high. When the conversations went deep as we confided our darkest secrets, the swing stilled, and our eyes locked.

Our friendship evolved as we started growing up. We each explored our identities. What defined us? A friend of her brother's teasingly declared Patty "the monster from the purple lagoon." She was no monster. Purple appropriately wrapped up the color of Patty's personality, so the name stuck. My best friend Patty became my best friend Purple.

> Purple appropriately wrapped up the color of Patty's personality, so the name stuck.

"What are you wearing to the Christmas party tonight?" I asked Purple.

"T-shirt and blue jeans. What else?"

"I was thinking of dressing up a little bit. This guy might be the one," I whispered into the phone. I didn't want to jinx my luck by saying it too loudly.

Purple made high school fun. She was a year older and helped me fit in. We sang in choir and musicals and worked hard to create the school newspaper and yearbook. We even received honors as the only charter members in our school's Quill and Scroll Society.

The Gift of Life Lessons

When you grow up with a person, you end up experiencing a lot of life with them. I have many fond memories, but I also think about the challenges made less challenging because of facing them together with Purple.

My first auto accident was as a passenger in Purple's 1960s Ford Falcon. It happened while we cruised down Georgia Street, a common small-town pastime. The driver in front of us came to an unexpected stop, and we slammed right into them. I remember the sudden shock of pain as I hit the dash (no seatbelts back then) and wondering, "What just happened?" We realized we needed to go to a home near the accident to call Purple's dad. She confessed what happened and asked him to come help. When he arrived on the scene, it was uncomfortable to face his disappointment in us. Talk about a quiet ride home!

Then there was the time we enjoyed an entire day spending our first hard-earned tax returns shopping at a mall. It was across the river in Quincy, the farthest distance from home I'd ever traveled with a friend. My parents trusted Patty—all the parents felt as if they had raised all of us together. (It takes a village!) What a glorious day of shopping, mall food, and watching a movie together.

We started the drive home after dark. In a little town just before we crossed the bridge toward home, a policeman pulled us over. We panicked—having heard the myth that cops there made you go to jail if you couldn't pay the fine on the spot. We rummaged through our purses to find some cash but had spent all our money that day. What were we going to do? Then Purple rolled down the window, and the officer said we had a taillight out. He instructed us to put on the car's flashers for the rest of the way home. We got off with a warning. Whew! Another "first" experienced with Purple.

The Gift of Engagement

As we matured, we began to get serious about our futures. Our boyfriends soon became our fiancées, and we planned a joint engagement party for when else—the Christmas season! It was fun to act the part of soon-to-be wives as we planned the menu, cooked the meal, and decorated the dining room for guests. Soon after the party, Purple's engagement was called off, but my wedding plans continued.

"Purple, will you be my maid of honor?"

"Of course!" she replied. "I would be mad if you asked anyone else."

What a friend! Even though we weren't planning our weddings together, she put her own life aside to be the maid of honor rather than the bride.

On our one-year wedding anniversary, my husband and I gathered with friends for a reunion. Purple met me at a restaurant before the party so we could squeeze in some girl talk.

"Kathy, you've put on a few pounds. Obviously, marriage agrees with you."

I just beamed. Only a best friend could tease me about gaining weight and get by with it! Giddy with catching up, we easily picked up where we had left off. Friendships like this are destined to last a lifetime.

> We easily picked up where we had left off. Friendships like this are destined to last a lifetime.

The Gift of a Phone Call

Many years passed without our traditional Christmas phone call. I sent out my annual Christmas newsletter to friends and family. Purple was on my mailing list, even though her name and address had changed. One year while I hung Christmas decorations, the phone rang. As I teetered on a chair to place an ornament near the back of the tree, Russ answered the phone.

"Why, yes! Kathy would welcome an interruption from you!"

Sensing the importance of this call, I hopped down from the chair to pick up the phone. I heard a polished voice say, "Hi, Kathy. This is Patricia. Do you remember me?"

Of course, I remembered her! My kid friend Patty, and my teen friend Purple, was now my adult friend Patricia. Once again, we picked up our conversation right where we had left off. We talked about her new husband and my new ministry. We caught up on all the family gossip and then promised to stay in touch.

A few years later, I flew across several states to speak at a Christmas tea ten miles from my hometown. I scanned the group for familiar faces as I shared Christmas memories during my program. In the message, I spoke about those magical Christmas phone calls with Patricia. Just as I mentioned her name, I discovered her eyes gleaming back at me from the audience. Imagine my joy—her presence made my holiday complete! I hustled to her table as soon as I finished speaking. Our friendship had endured twenty years of being apart.

The Gift of Eternity

Even though she is gone now, I grin when I think of our friendship. Not even death can separate friends when we can pick up right where we left off one day in heaven. The gift of friendship memories is one of the best gifts of all.

A Post-War Christmas Surprise

Delores Christian Liesner

L ITTLE PEOPLE HAVE BIG EARS," I heard one of my aunts whisper to my mom. Yes, I'd earned that distinction by being discovered more than once hiding behind a door, chair, or tree in order to gain more information.[3]

At seven, well-experienced at ferreting out secrets, I knew that Daddy, along with several dozen other townspeople, had been "called up" by the selective service when I was not even two. The story was oft repeated how loved ones had said goodbye and were standing in the town hall, hands raised to be sworn in, when the announcement came. The war had ended.

Daddy said when they were given the choice to stay and be sworn in or leave, "the place emptied in seconds." I also knew by the gaunt looks of many of those elders and neighbors that the effects of war, rationing, and the scarcity of jobs and income were slow to change.

Every penny counted in the years following the war.

That's why I now wondered what Mom meant when she whispered to Auntie, wondering what she would "do" for Christmas. If we only had a Christmas tree, I'd be happy.

Dad was in forestry, and in the past, he'd brought a tree home to decorate with paper chains and strings of popcorn. But now Dad couldn't afford a truck. So this year, Dad and Mom had decided to start a store in the living room!

First, they'd moved out the sofa and chairs and put a cooler in there, then a counter that had bins on the front. Some people Dad knew brought sausages and other meats that Dad would sell, and it sounded like they would both get money from doing it. The bins on the counter were for cookies. Not for us (we only got one when the man came to fill the bins), but mostly, they were there for the moms or dads who would come in to pick up meat. They often had children along and would buy them (and sometimes themselves) a cookie.

That went so well that Mom and Dad soon had more and more things added to the store, and Dad added shelves for the new items. Dad and Mom both looked pretty tired, but they looked happy too. One day, from behind the kitchen door on one of those deliveries, I heard Daddy tell the man he was going to take a financial risk and put a television in the store. I couldn't imagine where it would go. It was so crowded there was no room for anything else. Certainly not for the Christmas tree I wished for.

> It seemed the entire population of 500 came to see the TV.

The delivery man whispered to Daddy that he hoped the risk of purchasing a television would work to get people to come to our little store. It did work, likely because it was the first TV in town, and it seemed the entire population of 500 came to see the TV hooked up high on the wall across from the door. Most who came in purchased something while there. But if every penny had gone to get the TV and to have the little store stocked, there was likely to be no Christmas for our family that year.

We wanted to help Daddy and loved to go to the woods and work stacking pine boughs inside a four-cornered wood frame that looked like an X at the bottom. One branch would be laid toward the left side of the X, the next branch to the right, and so on. The bundles, tied with string and a big red bow, would be sold as grave blankets. We came home smelling like Christmas, which made us want a tree even more.

Tradition was to go to midnight church on Christmas Eve, and I loved seeing all the mysterious dark trees rising from the little nativity, some all the way to the ceiling of the church, all wearing blue lights. The music and the sermon were only background to the beautiful trees.

> The Christmas trees, to me, looked as though their hands were raised in praise and thanksgiving to God.

I don't know why I've always felt so emotional about trees. Maybe because somehow, they represented my daddy, who worked among them and taught me to respect and appreciate how they gave up their beauty to make so many things for us—like wood and paper. The Christmas trees, to me, looked as though their hands were raised in praise and thanksgiving to God, and I'd been comforted by their permanent greenery representing God and his everlasting love. I wanted a Christmas tree, but if these midnight moments were to be my Christmas, I was determined to enjoy every last second gazing at the bank of tall, tall trees on the left and the tiny one next to the manger while fighting a losing battle to lean against Mom or Dad and close my eyes for just a moment.

OF COURSE, WE SLEPT LONGER than usual on Christmas morning after being up so late. My sister, brother, and I tiptoed down the stairs but were dumbfounded to discover the stairwell door to our former living room, now grocery store, firmly locked.

Alarmed, all five of us banged on the door until Mom's voice on the other side said she would unlock the door after we sang some Christmas carols. It was fun to each start our favorite, be joined by the others, and then ask, "Now?"

Mom would say, "That was so pretty—just one more."

Finally, after Mom's favorite, "O Christmas Tree," the key turned, and the door slowly swung open. We gasped. Mom was standing in snow. Snow inside the house! (We later learned it was flour). Behind her were footprints, seemingly made by giant boots (Santa?), and we carefully obeyed her direction to "follow the footprints." Through the store, around the counter, passing shelves and cooler, back into the hall by the downstairs bedroom, and into the kitchen. Apparently, Santa had been here and searched for the tree as well.

Finally, the footsteps ended by the back door, where we could see the littlest tree from the nativity at church, now proudly standing in a mound of snow in the center of the backyard. Of course, we did not realize that Dad was the one who had provided the trees for church and arranged to bring home the little one after the service.

Our unison excited "Ohhhh!" acknowledged the beautiful and unexpected gift.

"After you open your stockings," Mom interrupted our awe of the sight, "you can make suet balls and decorate the tree." She then pointed behind us to the decorations we'd missed.

> We rolled chunks of suet in peanut butter, then tiny seeds, and tied the bird treats with red ribbons on the little tree.

Cheering, we ran to the stockings hanging on the back of the counter in the living room. I was amazed we'd passed so near them, unseeing in our excitement to follow the footprints. When you are young, much of life seems to be all about you, and perhaps that is why I did not feel surprised that the stockings were only for the children. More amazingly, I do not recall what was *in* the stockings except for fruit and nuts. I remember opening a little gift but was more eager to return to the kitchen, where we rolled chunks of suet in peanut butter, then tiny seeds, and tied the bird treats with red ribbons on the little tree.

It was a beautiful sight, and it wasn't long before "Christmas birds" showed up for their holiday treat. We had lunch (I no longer remember what we ate), played unnamed board games, and built puzzles of now-forgotten pictures. I still *do* remember how, from time to time, we would each steal out to the back door to watch the twice-used tree, alive with birds enjoying their Christmas treats.

Only in America, I thought years later, could that post-war Christmas be possible. Starting a home business on the strength of neighborly help and personal bartering or credit—no business plan, no bankers, no inspectors, or rentals of expensive buildings specially zoned for business. It didn't matter that nothing other than food in our "store" was new, and even our Christmas tree was slightly used. Everyone did what they had to do to survive, and everyone helped each other to get things done. It was a simple and less complicated time.

At the time, I just knew that Daddy hadn't had to go to war, our little store was providing for our needs, and it was Christmas inside and out!

Christ's Nativity

Lisa-Anne Wooldridge

The light passed from hand to hand.
In the dim sanctuary, a hush held sway,
Every heart waiting for
The coming of the light.

I stood beneath a stained-glass window
Adorned with fresh balsam fir
And bright red bows,
The green scent so different
From the honeyed acacia
Of a desert long-ago.
The humble wooden manger
Held no leafy boughs.

The church gilded what was plain,
A newborn baby nestled in rough hay
Was now wrapped with soft velvet throws.
I felt torn between two places,
One so warm and beautiful,
Sweet-smelling of cinnamon and cloves,
The other raw with biting cold, ripe with earth,
Livestock, and smoky haze.

O Holy Night,
We sang, but my wild heart
Resisted the tame indoor scene,
And parted ways with people dressed in silky clothes.
Longing for the babe, I fled my seat,
Hungry for crisp, clean air to breathe.
I hurried past all the legs—trying not to step on toes,
Until I lunged out the side door to feel the welcome relief
Of a scouring wind.

At the edge of the church garden,
I searched the skies,
The stars above me sat silent
But brilliant in their shining.
I looked for bright messengers
To bring me good news, but none showed.
My wet tears dried and still,
There was no whisper of angel song.

Oh, how I longed
For the light of the world to shine upon me.
My tender heart ached to touch the mystery
Of God with Us, Emmanuel.
Then I heard it, a new sound,
As the human chorus began to rise
Outside the hall, I strained to hear
The joyful glorias all around.

The bells began to ring, so I turned my face again
To the little church with the red door
That seemed to breathe with new, heavenly life.

A beautiful stained-glass glow bathed my face,
Light colored with the story
Of saints and angels from long ago.

Illuminated by candle flames,
The glorious shades of crimson,
Royal blue, and gold painted the snow
With good the news—the best news—
Of what the angels rejoiced to know.
And Suddenly,
The radiance of the Lord's glory
Was visible to me.
I knew that if I sought the Christ child,
I would find him,
Not inside the walls but in union
With the people they held,
Where he was born again,
Every heart a manger
Where he laid his sweet head.

I returned to my rest,
And to the people I loved,
Joining with them in the everlasting choirs.
Hark! The herald angels sing,
"Glory to the newborn King!"

Sleigh Bells and Shopping Bags

Hally J. Wells

NOT ALL TRADITIONS LAST A lifetime, but the best ones linger longest. Communities, countries, and family cultures are built around the regular, reliable activities and practices that take place during a year or season.

Of course, no other holiday lends itself to the establishment of traditions better than Christmas. Let's enumerate the ways! There are family cookie-baking days, tree-cutting adventures on snowy days, van-filled trips to see holiday light displays, viewing of Christmas plays, and vendor fair shopping days. Some sing Christmas carols at nursing homes, and others have ugly sweater parties. We give white elephant gifts and play "rob your neighbor." But of all those marvelous and splendid traditions, my absolute favorite is the girls' Christmas shopping weekend!

While the activity itself isn't all that original, the stories and memories each group of girls and set of sisters creates during shopping excursions are always unique to the ladies involved.

Hitting the Road

My mother, sister, and I shared our first official Christmas shopping weekend back in 1997. By late October of that year, I had finished my obligatory eight weeks of nursing my precious baby boy. I'd returned to work as a high school counselor, having completed my second year in the classroom as required by Missouri law, and was nearing completion of my master's in counseling. My sister had returned to Missouri after living in Texas for several years, and she was also back in school. And my mother had a middle-school son of her own. We all needed a little girl time!

We all needed a little girl time!

Off we went to Osage Beach (aka Lake of the Ozarks, Missouri) for an epic adventure of retail therapy—each purchase completely justified and without guilt since all were Christmas gifts and *had* to be bought.

Giggles and Going

One year, there was a large quilt store that offered huge discounts. Huge! The dizzying array of patterns and fabrics had a nearly hypnotic impact, and my mother got swept up in the bounty of bedding. Before long, she'd selected homespun bedspreads for no less than a dozen family members and friends; there were a few for personal use as well. Without much thought as to how the mountain of trash bags were going to fit into our van on the trek home, she purchased her picks.

Since I'm the older and nicer sister, I helped Mom schlep as many bags as we could out of the store during our first trip. However, we quickly got tickled at how we must have looked as we struggled with the heft of the Heftys. Embarrassed by my mom and me, my sister bolted and left us center stage between about a dozen stores, bent over in laughter and trying hard not to . . . you know.

Chuckles have that effect on us gals. Birthing ten-pound babies does too.

Some years into our string of shopping trips, my sister had delivered her second child. Born in October, he was a big boy! That year was rough. Without warning and the benefit of corrective bladder surgery, my sweet sissy had a couple of awkward incidents. My mother and I were once again laughing—this time as a *result* of a potty problem rather than the cause of one.

Behind the Wheel

When the three of us travel together, I am the designated driver. I generally have a good sense of direction, and I'm the one who most often owns a "mom van" suited for hauling home our finds.

Despite my respectable navigational skills, which I possessed way before we had cellular navigation, we have somehow managed to pass up a major exit on Interstate 70 on at least 20 percent of our trips. We get caught up in our chatting, and I've driven right by the giant billboard at Kingdom City and straight on toward Columbia, Missouri, before realizing I needed to turn around.

We often stay in one of two chain hotels. Our primary objectives are to find a place that offers a nourishing breakfast and a location close to the outlet mall—at one time, the mall we frequented boasted over one hundred retailers. One Saturday morning, after carb and protein loading, we were headed to the stores. The entrance to the hotel parking lot was very sloped. I sat in gear at the top of the incline and waited for an opening whereby I could exit the parking lot and enter the busy thoroughfare, which would deliver us to shopping heaven.

> When that opening appeared, I hit the gas . . .

Distracted by the lively post-breakfast discussion and review of lists and gift ideas, I failed to realize that I had the van in reverse. So, when that opening appeared and I hit the gas, I launched the bag-filled van and the three of us backward, downhill, and moving fast. Fortunately, no one was behind us!

Drama and Intrigue

Even though we have always enjoyed a lot of laughs on our shopping weekends, there have been serious moments too—tense, dramatic scenes when we've struggled to find just the right gift at just the right price. In the early years, my sister and I shopped for several cousins, and we'd stress for long periods of time in toy or children's clothing stores in an effort to score suitable gifts that fit into our young working-class budgets. Mom would eventually tell us to scoop up something and call it a day. We rewarded ourselves with Mexican or Italian dinners once we'd accomplished our holiday shopping feats.

Before retiring, Mom served as a county official for twenty-five years, and she had up to fifteen employees for whom she shopped each Christmas. She loved to identify a theme for the "employee gifts." For example, she might buy a pretty scarf for each of the ladies, making sure that no two were alike and, perhaps, each even had a connection with the recipient. It was a bit of a task.

One year, we nearly worked ourselves to death trying to find approximately fifteen unique pieces of Americana wall décor or tchotchkes at the Welcome Home store. Mom started gathering and assigning the items. "This is for Cindy, because . . ." and "I've chosen this for Dianne since she likes . . ." and "Do you think this looks like Karen?"

> It seemed we were never going to get them to fall into place. Certainly, not without a wall-sized Venn diagram!

You get the idea. Trying to find the right combination of similarly priced and themed gifts, with each matching the particular tastes of fifteen different girls—it was insane! Mom had all of her selections blocking the path between aisles, and it seemed we were never going to get them to fall into place. Certainly, not without a wall-sized Venn diagram!

Our Time

The years have brought changes to our routine. When the mall dried up, we moved our shopping weekends to Branson, Missouri. While we have become less energetic, we have also become blessed with a bit more free time. We have now extended our weekends from one overnight stay to often three nights. We relax more and shop a little less. The eating and laughing and joy of being together remain intact, and we'll keep making these trips for as long as we can.

My sister and I have two young adult daughters; they're pretty awesome. I also have a beautiful daughter-in-law and a gorgeous step-daughter. In recent years, I've asked if we shouldn't consider inviting them to join us. My hilarious and sassy sister insists that I must be smoking something when the subject comes up. I'm not. But, the truth of the matter is this. Our girls will have their time, but for right now, we love having that time with our mom. It is protected. It is our tradition and twenty-seven years strong! And it means the world to us.

Heart
and Home

Christmas Wheels

Michelle Rayburn

EAH EXITED THE SIDE DOOR of the church, slinging her laptop bag on her shoulder as she reached into her pocket for the remote for her minivan. She was always one of the last to leave the monthly gathering of aspiring Christian writers, but thanks to her delay, others had already left footprints to follow in the falling snow. Her fashionable leather ankle boots offered little for grip or warmth.

The glowing orbs of parking lot lights matched the afterglow in Leah's heart from being with her people. They got her. Understood her passion for crafting words and pursuing leads that offered little in the way of a paycheck. They cheered for meager publishing credits—letters to the editor, an article in the church bulletin, a magazine piece sold for fifteen dollars.

Leah stowed her tote bag on the passenger side floor, plowed her boots through the virgin snow around to the rear hatch, and searched for a windshield scraper.

"Oooh! Brr." Icy trickles melted down into her boots. *I sure wish I had remote start.* Leah closed the hatch and started clearing the windows. *Where did my mittens go?*

The last few stragglers from the meeting approached the remaining cars as Leah finished scraping. "See you next month," she called before tucking herself into the driver's seat. She let the vehicle idle a bit while she got situated. The usual forty-minute drive up north would likely take longer tonight.

Water bottle. Check. Seatbelt. Check. Snack. Wait—

She fished a protein bar out of her purse before texting Todd to let him know she was on her way.

By now, Leah's was the last car in the lot. She put the minivan in gear and eased on the gas. The engine stalled. *Noooo. Not today.* She turned the ignition key off and then on again. The green number 201930 illuminated beneath the speedometer dial as the usual instrument cluster startup sequence began. *High-mileage piece of rubbish is what it ought to read*, she thought.

Leah tried restarting a few more times with the same result—after a clunk and one promising lurch. *Hopeless.* Leah rested her forehead on the steering wheel.

Then she grabbed her cell to call Todd.

LEAH AND TODD WERE ON staff at a teen outdoor ministry, where Leah worked part-time in the office while finishing grad school, and Todd was the head of maintenance. They lived on the grounds in one of the homes provided for missionary staff. Their aging minivan was a godsend of a bargain when a friend offered it to them for trade-in value several years ago. It was perfect for the many times when young adult summer staff accompanied them to church or on shopping trips to town.

They'd already emptied their emergency fund to rebuild the transmission the year before. And Leah's desperate break-down calls had become more frequent. Some days, the van ran beautifully. Other times, she made last-minute apologies for why she wouldn't be able to make it somewhere.

Todd had access to a truck and a car hauler through the ministry— one bright side of the situation—but Leah's frustration smoldered as she hunkered down to wait for rescue yet again. *Lord, why did you call us here for work? Don't you see us? We're barely making ends meet. I know you've called me to write more and speak, but how? Why do we live in the middle of nowhere?* By now, the afterglow had after-gone.

THE MINIVAN STARTED UP THE next morning as if no incident had ever happened. Todd handed her the keys. "Good to go."

"Not exactly!"

"Well, I've tried everything. It's like it has a mind of its own."

Leah created a Marketplace listing in her head. *Used minivan. High mileage. Moderate rust. Balding tires. Runs on sunny days and when you don't have anywhere important to go.* She kissed Todd goodbye before heading to the den to study for her final exam. One more, and then she'd be on a long Christmas break until January.

Midday, Todd stopped by the house. "Say, hon, do you remember that couple we met at the outdoor ministry conference? Well, Ben called this morning about renting the facilities here, and in our conversation, I happened to mention your van troubles. A little while later, he called back and said he and Evelyn want to—maybe you should sit down—*give* us their van."

Leah felt goosebumps rise. "What?"

"Yeah. And get this. They talked about it with each other over a year ago when we first started raising missions support, but neither of them was sure we could use it. But then, last week, they again sensed God nudging them to give it away to someone. And they prayed for a clear sense of direction."

"And your conversation this morning was that clear direction?"

"Something like that. The crazy thing is that they didn't know why *we* kept coming to mind, but Ben had been moved by a sermon on sacrificial giving, and Evelyn heard something on the radio about being generous and stepping out in faith."

Leah thought about her recent whiny prayers. Maybe God had noticed her need after all.

"Leah, you listening?" Todd's voice broke through her thoughts. "Did you hear me say he wants us to come pick it up before Christmas?

DAYS LATER, LEAH STOOD ALONGSIDE Todd in Ben and Evelyn's garage, slackjawed as she fully understood the level of generosity. This was no cast-off clunker vehicle. The limited edition sporty black exterior with chrome accents, spotless interior, heated leather seats, television screen, all-wheel drive, and an odometer barely over 100,000 miles went far beyond anything Leah could have imagined.

"Come on inside so we can sign the title," Ben said.

"Can I get you any coffee? Tea?" Evelyn placed a plate of cutout cookies in the center of the table as Leah removed her coat and hung it on the back of a chair. Gingerbread men, snowflakes, and wreaths so exquisite they were art show worthy.

"Did you *make* these?" Leah asked.

Evelyn chuckled. "Our daughter's new hobby."

The two couples sat at the table as Evelyn explained how this had been a faith experience for their family. "Our teen son and daughter thought it was wild when Ben said we'd be giving away the van."

"But then they got really excited about it," Ben said. "It's brought us closer together as a couple. Prepared us to trust God too. We didn't—" He paused as his voice cracked.

Ben and Evelyn looked at one another.

Evelyn pressed her lips together and took a deep breath. "Ben got laid off permanently yesterday."

Leah gasped. "So close to Christmas," she said softly.

Todd started, "We can't possibly—"

Ben held up a hand and shook his head. "No. This is exactly what God wanted us to do—still wants us to do." He slid the title across the table, then reached for Evelyn's hand.

"I've been wrestling with this, Ben. It's kept me up at night," Todd said. "I've asked God how we can possibly accept such a generous gift, something that cost the two of you so much. But last night, God spoke to me while I lay there listening to Leah snore." She shot him a look. "I heard God ask, 'When was the last time you lost sleep over *my* gift?' God reminded me that his gift cost him everything."

He explained how, in the same spirit that surpassed logical sense when Jesus stepped from the splendor of heaven to a scratchy bed of straw, Ben and Evelyn had stepped outside of worldly common sense and obeyed God.

Leah looked at Todd with new admiration. He hadn't shared this struggle or revelation with her.

"That's the spirit of Christmas," Evelyn said. "It's about giving when it costs and humbly receiving something we don't deserve. It isn't the dollar amount but the personal cost."

Leah thought about what the cost would have been if, instead of discovering the news of Ben's job situation, they'd learned that he'd received an unexpected windfall from a bonus. Something that would make it easy to purchase a fancy new car and donate his old one. Suddenly, the magnitude of Jesus's birth made sense in a new way too. "The cost. He came to die, but he did it anyway," she whispered, her eyes shimmering with emotion. "Because of our need."

ON CHRISTMAS EVE, LEAH STARED out at the window as Todd navigated the winding road from the youth camp to the main highway. The evergreen branches hung low with the weight of another recent snowfall. Under her long wool coat, a toasty warmth on her backside reminded Leah of the benefits of the van's extra features.

The day before, a text from Ben to Todd had carried a message of hope, "New job! I start after New Year's."

Leah marveled at the impeccable timing, a testament to God's unwavering provision. *Lord, you continue to amaze me.* She looked forward to tonight's simple church service.

Todd broke the silence. "I'll never forget this surprise. We had nothing to put toward a new car, and yet here we are. Just like that first Christmas, when hope came to earth in the humblest of places."

It wasn't just wheels that Ben and Evelyn had given them. It was a reminder that God sees specific needs and provides generously. Their gift mirrored the ultimate gift of love that graced the world so long ago.

A smile danced across Leah's face like a flicker of candlelight in the darkened van. She adjusted the seatbelt carefully over her belly. *I hope Todd is ready for another surprise,* she thought. But that would have to wait. First, there were Christmas carols to sing and candles to light.

Lights in the Darkness

Heather Norman Smith

THE NIGHT WAS THE DARKEST I'd ever seen. Driving on unfamiliar roads, alone, with blackness all around, was like being in outer space. Anxiety took hold of me. I prayed and remembered the words printed on my bracelet, a gift from my sister—God's got this.

The new job had seemed like a miracle. After being told weeks earlier that the position was on hold, I received a call on a Thursday and was asked if I could start work the following Monday. The only problem was that I would have to leave on Tuesday, in just five days, for training out of state, and that would be the week before Christmas. With gifts still to buy and activities to plan for my family, the idea of a business trip was daunting. But a job with a software company—one that would allow me to work full-time from home after the short trip—was a blessing I couldn't pass up.

Gripping the steering wheel and fighting back tears as the dark night engulfed me and the miles stretched on, I had no regrets about my decision not to fly. I'm a mother. I like to be able to jump in the car and head right back to my babies if they need me. I wouldn't have had that kind of control if I'd taken a plane. The trip was for only two nights, but leaving my four children—two boys and two girls ranging in age from three to thirteen—even safe at home with their father, had been hard. It was so hard, in fact, that I had waited until late in the afternoon to start the journey, even though it meant the six-hour drive—my longest solo road trip—would be done mostly at night.

After six hours of driving, my nerves were frazzled, and the GPS said I still had an hour left to go. Then, the app on my phone routed me away from the familiarity of the interstate to two-lane, winding roads. If I had studied the geography of the route, I wouldn't have been so surprised by all the mountains between my home in North Carolina and my destination in Maryland, but the terrain was not what I had expected, and now I couldn't see any of it. I could have been driving along the edge of a cliff and wouldn't have known.

How long could there be nothing but blackness? The only thing I could see was the road as far ahead as the headlight beams. No houses, no trees, no stores, no other cars, and no landmarks of any kind. It seemed like ages since I'd even seen a traffic sign. Whatever was out there was shrouded in darkness.

I leaned in close to the steering wheel. My breaths came fast. The temperature outside hovered near freezing, and a light mist covered the windshield. There was nowhere to pull over if the weather turned bad. What if my phone's battery died? What if I lost signal? How would I get help when I couldn't see *anything* in this impossible darkness?

I prayed again for peace. "God's got this. God's got this," I told myself.

Then my eye caught something in the distance. The faintest glimmer. Finally! It was *light*! The light appeared to be coming from a house up ahead. The house was lit up for Christmas! I wasn't in outer space. I wasn't alone. Someone was nearby. I didn't know them, but they celebrated the season like I did. Maybe a family like mine lived there, with kids anticipating Christmas morning. The homeowner couldn't have known what the colored lights along their roofline meant to me. That simple string of Christmas lights was a beacon of hope, and my anxiety subsided at the sight of it, replaced by an unexpected comfort.

When I reached Frederick, Maryland, and finally the hotel very late that night, I was grateful not only to have arrived but also for the journey. The Christmas lights in the dark night had reminded me of the reason we celebrate—Light shined in a dark world to give us hope. When it looked as though sin had overshadowed everything, Jesus's presence illuminated mankind's dire condition with the truth of God's love. When it seemed the long, black night would never end, the Daystar shined and pointed the way to the Father. Isaiah 9:2 says, "The people who walk in darkness will see a great light. For those who live in a land of deep darkness, a light will shine."

> I want my life and the joy he's given me to be a beacon of hope to those who feel lost in darkness.

My experience also reminded me of the great privilege I have of sharing God's light with the world to give others hope. All year round, and especially at Christmas, I pray that his light shines through me. I want my life and the joy he's given me to be a beacon of hope to those who feel lost in darkness. Matthew 5:14–16 says, "You are the light of the world—like a city on a hilltop that cannot be hidden. No one lights a lamp and then puts it under a basket. Instead, a lamp is placed on a stand, where it gives light to everyone in the house. In the same way, let your good deeds shine out for all to see, so that everyone will praise your heavenly Father." The simple Christmas lights on a house roof had given me confidence in my direction and reminded me that I can help guide others toward the true reason for the season by showing them his love.

As I settled into the comfortable hotel room, even in my exhaustion, my mind whirred, thinking of ways to shine the light of Christ—simple acts of kindness like baking cookies for a neighbor or sincere words like "I'm praying for you" spoken to someone who was hurting. Even saying "Merry Christmas" with a smile on my face could brighten the darkness. What a wonderful opportunity the season offered. I had a renewed purpose to let my own "Christmas lights" shine.

After spending two days training and meeting some of my nice new co-workers, I headed home. Tiny snowflakes fell from the sky as I crossed from Maryland into West Virginia, and in the early afternoon light, I saw the beautiful country that had been cloaked by night on the trip there. I was mesmerized. *I drove through this?* I really had no idea what beauty awaited when night was over.

It was dark by the time I neared the North Carolina state line a few hours later, and in my anxiousness to get home to hug my children, my foot weighed on the gas pedal heavier than it should have. As I cruised down the mountain, blinding blue lights illuminated the night. They *weren't* Christmas lights. My homecoming would be delayed by at least a few more minutes.

I eased the car onto the shoulder of the road and steadied myself. It had been years since I'd been pulled over by a police officer. Thankfully, the Virginia civil servant who stopped me for speeding well over the limit had a kind and gentle demeanor, and he put me at ease right away. He was gracious when I apologized for speeding *and* when I explained my hurry to get home after my business trip. Still, I expected a ticket. I certainly deserved one.

The officer took my license and registration back to his patrol car, and after what seemed like a long time, he leaned near the car window again. His kind eyes reflected the light coming from inside my minivan. To my relief and surprise, he said, "I'm going to let you go with a warning this time," and he cautioned me to slow down the rest of the way home. It was the second Christmas miracle of my trip! And it was another reminder of what Christmas is all about. Jesus came to earth to offer a pardon for my sin, even though I didn't deserve it. My journey north had been a lesson about hope, and the journey home taught me about mercy.

I pulled into my driveway within an hour after my run-in with the law, and inside the house, in the glow of the Christmas tree, I wrapped my arms around each of my four children. My heart swelled with gratitude for being home and being with them, for the lessons I'd learned because of lights in the darkness, and for the gifts of hope and mercy. The two-day business trip had prepared my heart for Christmas in ways only God could have known.

Delivering Christmas

Joni Topper

WALKED DOWN THE STREETS OF Austin, Texas, on Christmas Eve, tears dripping off my chin. I couldn't wipe them away because my hands were full of letters. Totally beyond my control, those tears possessed a mind of their own. I kept telling myself to focus on the fact that by delivering mail, I also brought joy. In those days before the prominent one-day delivery option existed, parents often waited in suspense for that last-minute package intended to delight their child. All I could focus on that day were my own six-, eight-, and ten-year-old children who were waiting for me at home—where I should be.

I took a job at the U.S. Postal Service, thinking if I started work at 5:00 a.m. each day, I would be home to greet my kids when they got off the bus after school. It never seemed to work out that way. I left for work before they rose in the morning and got home long after their school day ended.

When my name appeared on the schedule for Thanksgiving Day the first year I worked there, my heart sank. Just like most places of employment, the new kid does not get holidays off. Someone has to hold down the fort while those with seniority take off. Now, a month later, I found myself working on Christmas Eve too.

To make matters worse, my assignment changed every day. My route for the day was revealed each morning. Only a map kept me from weaving up and down the streets aimlessly. Walking those unfamiliar places, I passed kids playing in their front yards. Smells wafted from the front doors of homes where families laughed in the kitchen while they prepared their favorite holiday meals.

> The home, the husband, the children—the whole picture was in place, yet I was not there.

I felt like a distant observer of the world. My wonderful life existed, yet I was unable to participate in it due to this task of making everyone else's Christmas merry. The home, the husband, the children—the whole picture was in place, yet I was not there. Why was I spending Christmas Eve in an unfamiliar part of town, miles from my family, when in so many ways, my life mimicked a Hallmark movie?

Different Address

Three years before, my little family moved three hundred miles away from our hometown. Ernest and I were working hard to blend our family and create wholeness from the previous disarray of our lives. The first Christmas in our new setting, we were not settled into our house. The second year, we traveled back to our roots. This year, my target had been to make our new place feel like home.

So much for festivities. I just needed to *get* home at this point, clean up, and figure out something I could disguise as dinner. I could just cover the basics, clean the toilet, and not worry about a feast. My commute back home took fifty minutes if the traffic flowed smoothly.

All the way home, I tried to correlate the idea of Mary—riding a donkey, nine months pregnant, merely a teenager—with my situation. There was no pertinent link I could think of that would make me feel noble about this sacrifice. She was in misery. I was in misery. Her discomfort would deliver the Christ child. Mine would help keep our family out of financial ruin. It felt petty to even compare the two, but I looked for some meaning that might give my dismay a holy luster.

Different Setting

I tried to compose myself before walking into the house, knowing that I possessed the power to create either a loving atmosphere or a bitter one with these children I'd longed for all day. After that long drive, it took all the fortitude I could muster to walk in with a smile. I knew the cleaning, cooking, gift wrapping, and needy kids would face me when I crossed the threshold. That's not even close to what happened.

"Joni, why don't you go take a shower and rest. The kids and I are getting dinner ready."

What?

In that moment, I realized I had not even taken a good inventory of my kitchen. The hours I'd spent fretting should have been spent doing some mental food prep. What kind of mother does not plan food for the holiday?

The frustration I'd felt all day disappeared in my shock. My husband greeted me gently and steered me toward the bedroom. When I smelled the delightful meal that he and the kids masterminded together, even my perceived failure as a homemaker dissipated.

Pulling my sweaty socks off, I felt relief replace my anxiety. Ernest gave me a while to get cleaned up, then stuck his head in the room. "The kids are wearing their best clothes. You can too if you want to. Dinner will be another thirty minutes or so."

"Okay. Thanks." Even relaxing took effort, but I stilled myself, taking in the moment for what it was—a gift.

When dinner was ready, all three kids came to get me. They were clean and dressed like they were going somewhere special.

They were. To our very first family tradition, which we named the "Christmas Eve Feast." For our little brood, it felt huge.

Following our noses toward the kitchen, we passed the kids' rooms. I noticed that they were tidy. Someone had run the vacuum cleaner and dusted the furniture. Even the bathroom mirror was clean, no water spots from messy little hands. In the living room, the tree stood as a declaration of grace, surrounded by neatly wrapped gifts and poinsettias.

My favorite red plaid Christmas tablecloth and cloth napkins lay in perfect order on the table. "Mom, you sit here. I made us name place cards." Crystal said, even then, a little hostess at heart.

"I'll light the candles." Emily took charge of carefully handling the matches. Soon the red candles flickered, standing at attention as though they had been anxiously awaiting their turn to shine.

Little Rodney walked around the table, offering each person a hot roll. "There's butter, too, Mom."

A butler could not have presented a more perfect table. Each piece of silverware adorned its place with perfect correlation to the plates. The tea glasses sparkled and reflected the motion of flickering candlelight. All the serving dishes coordinated with the dinner plates. Our country bumpkin table looked as if it had been to finishing school.

> If someone had declared the holidays were over at the end of that meal, I would not have felt shortchanged.

Ernest served each member of the family after we were seated. Cornish hens baked with a lovely tint to the skin, mashed potatoes with a pool of butter on top, green peas, salad, deviled eggs, pickles, olives, cheese, and more hot rolls set up my expectations for the final course. Dessert. Chocolate cake with chocolate icing crowned our feast. We all knew this moment would live in our collection of precious family memories. If someone had declared the holidays were over at the end of that meal, I would not have felt shortchanged.

Different Season

Through the years, situations have changed. The kids grew up and started their own family traditions. Some of them live in other towns now, but all of us cherish those Christmas Eve feasts. The feast that was born on the heels of what felt like a less-than-perfect day.

Our family feast tradition continued during those years of my postal career that required me to work on Christmas Eve. As our family dynamics shifted, I began participating in the preparations for the meal. Each occasion provoked a light step in me, a thankful spirit that I could be home.

Instead of being needy kids that day, my children found joy in serving. Our Christmas Eve feast solidified that lesson. Each of them delighted in doing their part because they were celebrating the birth of Jesus, *and* they were helping me. We all benefited from my husband's wisdom in coordinating the effort.

Different Home

The most impressive part of the Christmas story to me is that Jesus *left* the perfect home. He took a detour from heaven to deliver us hope. He left the very place we long to be. Heaven. I longed to be home. He must have longed to be back home too. He *left* the presence of God to show us the way to a heavenly home. He even designed an earthly family to help us along the journey.

I love this story because it reminds me that Jesus is in the background preparing a feast for me. When this life does not deliver what I imagined as perfect, he's preparing a better homecoming than I could have imagined.

That year, my family repurposed a lousy day and remade it into a celebration. Jesus did the same thing the day he delivered Christmas.

Air in These Busted Tires

Heidi Vertrees

C HRISTMAS EVE. I GAWKED AT the flat tires on my mother's car and zipped my jacket tighter. I let out a deep breath into the cold air. Several days ago, I had flown in from Maryland to visit my family in Colorado, especially my much loved, ninety-five-year-old mother. We all knew these were precious days to be with her. Our father had passed on five years earlier.

Now darkness was descending, and I was alone under a bridge by the side of a thruway near Denver International Airport. Snow circled around with plenty more on the ground. I wasn't dreaming of *this* white Christmas. What was I going to do?

Moments earlier, I'd seen on the big screen at the cell phone lot that my sister's flight had finally arrived. I was so excited to greet her. I didn't even wait for her call. I sped as fast as allowed but noticed my dry eyes troubling my vision. I pulled into a car rental lot to stop and squirt my eyes with eye drops. Apparently, I needed more than eye drops.

Ever Make a Wrong Detour in Life?

What did I know about car rental lots at airports? Sure, I had traveled around the world, but I didn't rent cars at airports. As I exited, I saw those unfamiliar yellow pieces low to the ground that I had crossed to enter. But this time, they made a sudden swish, swish sound. *What was that?* I worried.

At the next red light, my sister called.

"I'm super close!" I rang out, hopeful, but now cheery was a stretch.

When I got the green, my mother's usually faithful car clumped forward. Time to pull over. *Time to pray.* Despair enwrapped me. How would I get my sister now? How would we take my mother to her longed-for Christmas Eve church service?

Dear God, I feel so stupid. That lot had ground barricades to stop thieves from escaping with returned rental cars. Sometimes in life, we make wrong detours.

A driver pulled over and offered to help. He took one sympathetic look at the tires and encouraged me to call for bigger help. But God was already "on the job." He always is. I just was momentarily too distraught to sense his arrival.

I gathered up my gumption and reached for my cell phone. Time to break the news to my big sister. Time to feel more stupid.

"Hi, Lea. There's going to be a delay. I got a flat. More than one!"

"Oh, no! Are you okay? Wait! I'll give you my AAA membership number. That might help you for the tow. I'll sit inside till I hear from you."

Always the gracious sister.

How to Fix This Mess?

The tow truck that pulled up was not just an ordinary tow truck. As my eyes trailed the length of the flatbed, my heart sank. I didn't just make a mess for this Christmas Eve. I made a BIG mess. With God's help, how was I going to fix things?

It seemed miraculous that the driver got our "sunken ship" on the flatbed and strapped it down. I called my sister.

"Lea, which door will you be near?" Our plan had been to meet her on a curbside by the terminal.

Once we set our meeting point, I added, "You'll have no problem recognizing us!" We both laughed. After all the tension, it felt good. We wouldn't quite be Santa's sleigh pulling up, but we sure would attract some attention.

Some older sisters would have made a younger sister feel bad by now. Instead, Lea and I were so happy to see each other when our "stagecoach" pulled into the station. She had flown in from Texas. Both of us were making a big effort to be together, and we didn't want a bunch of busted tires ruining our sweet family reunion and Christmas celebration.

Our driver hoisted Lea's luggage into the cab and helped her clamber up inside, where she slipped into the back seat. Okay, as I had to spill the details, I am sure there was some silent headshaking from the back.

As we traveled toward Boulder, we chatted with the driver.

"Do you have any plans for celebrating Christmas?" my sister asked.

"I sure look forward to seeing my young girls later tonight."

He was planning to head home after he dropped us off at an auto repair shop where my younger brother would get us. I looked at my watch. My mental clock whirred as I thought about what little time we had before the Christmas Eve service.

"The service starts at—"

Before I could finish my sentence, my sister leaned forward. "Heidi, there just isn't time!"

But the elf was out of the bag. "Where are you trying to go?" our kind driver asked.

> Didn't we all know some sadness that can stick on some holidays, like the snow gathering on the truck window, making our view of life smudgy?

Thinking of our mother's desires, I blurted, "We had plans to take our mother to the Christmas Eve service at her church. It may very well be the last one she ever goes to, and it means so much to all of us to take her there. I am so sorry I have made a mess of things."

Everyone got quiet. Didn't we all know some sadness that can stick on some holidays, like the snow gathering on the truck window, making our view of life smudgy? By the driver's guarded tone before, I figured he didn't always see his children, and I wanted him to get done working soon so he could see them for Christmas.

His eyes remained fixed on the highway. "Where does your mother live?"

When we told him, he said, "Let's go there instead. The repair shop will be closed by now. Your mom's house is close enough." He paused, but before we could reply, he closed the deal. "It would make me feel good to help you since it's Christmas." I think all our hearts started to glow, and God's love was in the cab too.

> I think all our hearts started to glow, and God's love was in the cab too.

We had already phoned my mother and brother to let them know of our predicament. I could hardly wait to call them again. We all looked at our preferred timepieces and wondered how God would manage the minutes we had.

This time, big sister placed the call. No room for more delays. Time to set everything in high gear. And God, please let there be time to pump us full of rejoicing?

"Hi, Jon. Can you get Mom ready for church and warm up your car, please? We will be there soon, and we'll need to go straight away to make the Christmas Eve service."

Maneuvering our dear mother meant helping her get from her rocker to her walker to quickly put on her warm winter coat before helping her into her wheelchair. She would plunk her hat on her head and be thrilled with our plans.

As we entered my mother's neighborhood, Lea texted Jon of our arrival.

When the driver came to a stop at our agreed-upon spot for unloading my mother's car, I turned to him. "Thank you for everything you've done for our family. We hope you also have a wonderful Christmas."

"Yes! Thank you so much! Merry Christmas!" Lea chimed in from the back seat.

Our driver smiled. "Merry Christmas to all of you!"

> Their happiness and excitement filled the air. More air for busted tires.

We said our goodbyes as he helped us to the ground. Lea and I rushed up the short driveway while our driver carried Lea's suitcase for her. When he set it down by the garage, he gave a quick wave and turned to go. In the opened garage, we saw our mother and Jon at the top of the wheelchair ramp that led from the house. Their happiness and excitement filled the air. More air for busted tires.

Even though our mother could no longer walk, she remained the most big-hearted and wise woman I have ever known. God made her sturdy on the inside, and her smile was endless.

After hugs and kisses, we got into my brother's warmed-up car and headed to the church.

O, Holy Night

My mother's church is nestled in the foothills on the southwestern edge of Boulder. With the snow all about and the church lights shining as we approached, I felt bedazzled by the beauty. My brother parked by the curb so we could remove the wheelchair from the back and prepare our mother for the closest route inside. The service was just beginning. It would have been rude to enter in the front. But that was the only way in with a wheelchair, wasn't it?

Then, for the first time, we noticed a small side door.

"Let's try it," Mom said.

Jon opened the door to the sounds of robust singing and smiles from familiar faces. To our surprise, the spot by this door had a cutaway in the pew, which was intended just for a worshipper in a wheelchair. Guess who? We could not have had an easier time sitting together as a family in a crowded church on Christmas Eve. God had indeed refilled our near-busted souls. We rejoiced together, remembering our dear Savior's birth.

Jesus Understands Messes

The preacher began the sermon. Wouldn't you know it? She preached on how messy the first Christmas had to have been. Mary and Joseph were far from home, and Mary was in no condition to travel. Then, in Bethlehem, there was no room for Mary to give birth but among barn animals and no bed for baby Jesus but a manger.

"Sometimes our lives get messy too."

She could have been looking directly at us, even though we sat halfway back in the church, so grateful to be there.

"God loves us and wants all of us, even with our messes in life. He can clean us up and make our lives better."

And God just had.

Miles Apart, Forever in the Heart

Pam Fields

WITH A STUBBORN POUT, I stormed through the house. I admit it. I was mad. Our son didn't make it home for Christmas, and now everyone wanted to take a family photo. Without him! How could we take a photo when someone was missing? How could we just pretend that he wasn't part of our family? Of course, he was part of our family, but his military service detained him and created a separation that year.

He was supposed to be home. They'd promised him he would be home for Christmas after boot camp. But as we were learning, the surest promises in military life are often wishful thoughts.

The Launch

Ben was barely eighteen years old when he left for boot camp. He was very careful to select the week that he would sign papers, calculating the length of travel and training to make sure that things would be wrapped up just in time for holiday leave. It was perfectly mapped out. Sixteen weeks of boot camp and AIT (Advanced Individual Training) at Fort Benning, Georgia. Graduation, December 7. Perfect timing to transfer to his permanent duty station and then to be released for vacation.

Visions of the warm summer days as they crept into fall are clearly etched in my mind. Though preserving food was part of my yearly routine, there was something very different about it this year. Near the end of August, my second son moved out. It wasn't just getting an apartment or heading off to college. It's not that those aren't life-changing, but this, this was dangerous. This was a pledge to give all, even his life for his country, and it wrecked me.

Before the army entered our lives, I wasn't much of a crier. I didn't really "do" emotions. But somehow, when he raised his right hand and swore an oath, my life changed. It wasn't just Hallmark movies but laundry soap commercials that could break me. Memories played through my mind with little prompting, and the wave that carried them in typically washed them out in a flood of tears.

> It was a new season. A season of release and a season of growth for all of us.

I didn't understand how to process my emotions, but I did know how to process a harvest. Knowing that I needed to keep my hands busy to calm my racing mind, I purchased crates of tomatoes, dozens of green peppers, onions, and garlic. As I stood in the kitchen for countless hours, my mind was free to wander. When my younger children approached and saw me crying, I pointed to the pile of produce and told them, "It's just the onions." But they knew.

They knew that mom was heartbroken. It was a new season. A season of release and a season of growth for all of us. I was proud of my son and not surprised at all that he had joined the military. I had full confidence that he was exactly where he needed to be. Yet, it was a hard adjustment.

Connection

Though we knew it was protocol, within hours of dropping him off at MEPS (Military Entrance Processing Station), he surrendered his phone to his commanding officers, and all communication ceased. We get so used to talking to our kids, sending a quick message, meme, or emoji that it becomes second nature. At times, it seems impersonal to communicate through text. Though as detached as it may seem, it is still a connection. When the line goes cold, when there are no read receipts, no thumbs up, no response, it is chilling. As if they have dropped off the planet. I had to remind myself that he hadn't been kidnapped. He was simply preparing to serve.

> As my thoughts lingered and were carried away, they were carried into prayer.

As my thoughts lingered and were carried away, they were carried into prayer. As I gazed down the tree-filled lane while the spaghetti sauce simmered and the pressure canner slowly came to temperature, I held on to what I knew to be true. I knew that God, in his sovereignty, had my boy—ahem—my young man in his sight and the palm of his hand, even though he wasn't in mine.

Eventually, there was a rhythm to the days and a peace that I could find in our new life. Nearly every day, someone from our house would craft a letter, draw a picture, or have a photo printed to send in a letter to the training center. We looked for news from our town and from Ben's classmates that we could share with him. I scoured the army mom support groups online for suggestions of what to put in a care package and, sometimes, more importantly, what not to put in! This was a new normal. A new way to keep in touch.

I didn't doubt our ability in a household of nine to be able to fill the envelopes that traveled 2,000 miles east to Fort Benning. What surprised me and brought absolute delight were the many letters that arrived coming west to Oregon. Though the days of training were full and personal free time limited, Ben faithfully recorded and recounted the training exercises and his experiences, sharing them with us each step of the way. At times, we were overwhelmed by the rigor and challenges that he faced, but at the same time, it gave us confidence in his training. We were assured that he was being prepared to serve as a defender of freedom with the best military in the world.

In those letters, I saw the formation of a man and a glimmer of the little boy that I once held in my arms. He had a genuine curiosity about the events at home and requested photos of all his siblings. We delivered. Others may wonder why I printed the photo of a smoldering loaf of garlic bread blackened by the char of the broiler. It was for his amusement as he guessed which of his younger siblings oversaw dinner that night. Photos of friends from church, sporting events, family gatherings, and of some of our meals provided a link between the only world he had ever known and the one that was now his domain.

> The countdown was on, and the letters became less about training and more about coming home.

As the weeks on the calendar progressed, the anticipation of a reunion was being shaped. The countdown was on, and the letters became less about training and more about coming home. Tucked into practical information about travel arrangements and the graduation ceremony were dreams. Each letter revealed more expectancy about the days that he would be able to spend with family in his childhood home. There were lists. Not only was he dreaming of time away from the strenuous training, but he was also dreaming of food. Lots of food! Homemade meals made with my spaghetti sauce and time spent around the table with loved ones.

Reunited

Absence and longing will make one rise to new challenges. It had been twenty years since I had been on an airplane, which, at one point, I had resolved to be a permanent situation. My fear of flying tormented me as I was tossed between my psychological safety and being able to hug my son. As you may guess, I found my resolve, tightly squeezed my husband's hand, and closed my eyes as we sped down the runway. My tears of separation led to tears of anxiety, but I knew what was coming: tears of joy.

> My tears of separation led to tears of anxiety, but I knew what was coming: tears of joy.

With pride, hundreds of soldiers represented their units and the accomplishments they had made over previous months. The moment was matched by the pride of thousands of friends and family in the stands— loved ones who held the graduates in the highest esteem as we looked on. There was no division in that crowd. Not geographic, socio-economic, racial, religious, or any other kind imaginable. The national anthem played, and there was a universal and palatable depth to what we shared, knowing what this ceremony signified.

Graduates tossed hats in celebration, and the bleachers cleared quickly as we rushed to the field to find our soldiers. The expressions on their faces that were just moments before chiseled and firm now softened as eyes connected in the crowd. Smiles, hugs, tears. We made it through. Within thirty minutes, our children, our heroes, were ushered onto buses holding their rucksacks and precious memories. They were on to their first assignment.

If planned as a crash course in survival or by mere oversight, the long bus ride to the new base ended abruptly. After sixteen weeks of micromanagement and oversight from commanding officers, the recruits were dropped at the welcome center on their new base with absolutely no instructions. There were no room assignments, no hot meals, and no showers to tidy up after a long day. They did what they were taught to do: find a place in the hallway on the cold, hard ground and make a pillow from their duffel bag.

December 7th graduation. Check. December 8th new duty station. Check. Assignment to new unit and then release for vacation? Not so fast.

Due to some terrible breakdown in communication, these new soldiers, eager for home, received the news that vacation had already started for their new units, and there was no one on base to sign their papers for leave.

With their phones back in their possession, news traveled across the miles. Waiting for the details to change, waiting for someone to fix this mess. Days passed, weeks. Mothers shopped, cooked, and prepared their homes, dreaming of a secret homecoming surprise to be unveiled.

December 23. December 24. Then Christmas morning. As we made Facetime calls on that sad and lonely day, we knew that our circumstances weren't changing. Smiling on the outside but ugly tears within, we tried to hold it together. #Armystrong. Christmas was now past.

Celebration

On December 29, the photographer arrived. Though my feet moved through the house to collect the 8x10 photo of Ben in his dress blue uniform, my heart was firmly planted on the couch in a big puddle of self-pity. If we couldn't all be in the family photo, at least I would hold his image.

I couldn't have been more upset at my eldest son, who managed to be late for the photo shoot. I just wanted it done and over with. I was never going to put the photo up anyway. I was never going to look at it. After Caleb came screaming up the driveway and parked, he lined up with the rest of us.

Then, through the trees, wearing camo and a great big smile, my soldier came running! Though the flights were delayed, and the traffic was ridiculous, my boys managed to pull off the best Christmas surprise of my life. No, it didn't happen on December 25, but he was home. All hearts come home for Christmas, and ours were full.

A Merry Belated Christmas

Charlaine Martin

"Y OU CAN'T BE SERIOUS!" I protested. The customer service representative kindly informed me that the Christmas gift I ordered was backordered—again. I purchased my husband's Christmas gift online in September. Still, I kept getting out-of-stock notices from the online retailer, thinking it would be delivered in time. This gift would be perfect for him if only it would arrive for Christmas.

"I'm sorry, ma'am. These have been selling faster than we anticipated. The company is struggling to keep up with the demand. You should receive it by December 24," she assured me with an apologetic tone. "Is there anything else I can do for you?"

"No, I suppose not. Thank you." I hung up, feeling let down. *What will I do if it's not here by Christmas Eve?* I pondered, hoping a plan B would magically pop into my head. I only had two more weeks to get everything ready.

I'D ALWAYS PRIDED MYSELF ON getting or making gifts that my family wanted or that I thought would be perfect for them. This year, buying gifts challenged us more than expected. Our funds were tight since church attendance was down, so our tiny church struggled to pay their pastor, my husband, Don, regularly. I filled in for other instructors and lifeguards at the YMCA, so the extra money I earned helped soften the pinch.

> This year, buying gifts challenged us more than expected.

One afternoon, I returned from work with the kids' presents I'd gotten out of layaway at our local discount store. Since I left work early, I quickly wrapped their gifts and put them under the Christmas tree in front of the picture window. The sunlight glittered off the ornaments and streamed in as I cut, taped, and tagged each one. Suddenly, I heard someone's key in the front door lock. As I rushed to tape the last package, my teenage kids piled into our house, their backpacks dusted with snow while our little dog wagged her tail, waiting for pets.

"Hi, Mom," one daughter greeted me, glancing at the paper and ribbon strewn across the floor around the last package. "Do we need to close our eyes?" she asked.

"No, I'm done. How was school?"

"Oh, it was good," my son replied, telling me about his day as he removed his coat and boots. All three shared Christmas concert information, classes, and friend updates while I gathered my Christmas mess. They piled their coats on the bench by the door and set their boots in a dirt-tinged puddle on the entry floor.

"What would you like for Christmas dinner?" I inquired. "I'll stop at the store tomorrow to pick up the ham, cranberries, and rolls."

Their eyes lit up. "How about your baked mac and cheese? Please?" my son pleaded.

The girls chimed in, "Yes!" and made their requests as they foraged for afterschool snacks, with our dog trotting behind them.

I jotted down their requests on my grocery list. They loved that I found ways to reduce food misery for holiday meals. Don ate most of what I cooked, but I knew his favorites after all these years.

"Kids, I'm at a loss about your dad's gift since his is backordered. It might not get here in time. Any suggestions?" I hoped they might have some ideas.

My older daughter suggested something musical since she and her dad shared a love of music. My son thought something karate-related since we taught Christian martial arts at our church. My youngest daughter offered an idea for puzzles, but not the jigsaw kind. "It's too bad you're having such a difficult time getting what you wanted for him," she sighed.

"It's okay," I said. It really wasn't, but there was nothing more I could do but wait.

Navigating the Christmas Rush

The next day after work, I wound my way around some Amish women who piled into the grocery store with their carts blocking off the hams and turkeys. *All I want is one ham, for Pete's sake!* I snagged one as a woman dressed in a charcoal gray dress gave me a smug glare. *Cha-ching!* I smiled as I dashed to the checkout with our Christmas food, ready to get my plan B gift for Don.

Nearing the checkout of our local discount store with a master-level strategy puzzle in my cart, I took my place in the long line of last-minute shoppers. I had always avoided stores that close to Jesus's birthday, but at least I had something Don would enjoy.

WHEN I CAME HOME, I hoped that Don's present would await me on our doorstep. Instead, I discovered a notice in our mailbox stating this prized gift was now delayed until after the New Year—January 15! I rolled my eyes, groaning. At least I had a puzzle Don would love. I quickly wrapped it and stuck it under the tree.

Christmas day went beautifully, as it usually did. Everyone enjoyed the gifts they received and the responses to the presents they gave. Inside, I felt disappointment as Don opened his. "I love it! How did you know I wanted this one?" His eyes twinkled as he began working it toward a solution, with Christmas paper piled at his feet.

"I'm sorry, Hon," I apologized. "The gift I ordered won't be here until next month."

He looked at me, showing concern, "Sweetheart, it's okay. We have each other, a roof over our heads, and food on the table—very good, I might add."

I smiled. Don was right. *Thank you, God, for family together and our needs met.* Christmas was perfect because of him, not what we could give each other. I sipped my peppermint tea, smiling as we read the Christmas story together. Sometimes my perfectionism and my love language of gifting clouded my thoughts. That's one of the many reasons I loved Don so much.

Late Arrival Right on Time

I continued receiving backorder notices for Don's belated Christmas gift. *At least his birthday is at the end of January,* I thought. I would give it to him then. Then another message later said it would arrive in February. Sigh. *I'll give it to him for Valentine's Day. Oh, well.* I dashed out to get him a Buckeye sweatshirt he liked—since he graduated from Ohio State and loved their football team.

> Strangely, Valentine's Day became Christmas!

Strangely, Valentine's Day became Christmas! I spied a large, flat box waiting on our porch when I pulled up in front of our home. I took it inside, opened it enough to peek in, and check that the snow hadn't ruined it. *Nope!* Smiling big, I retaped the box and set it up on the arms of a living room chair to greet him when he came in the door.

When he arrived home, he immediately noticed the box. "What's this?" he queried, curiously checking it out.

"Come open it! It's what I've been waiting on for so long." I could scarcely contain my excitement.

He peeled back the tape, opened it, and stood stunned, looking the painting over. "Oh, it's beautiful!" But there was also a smaller box inside with the artwork.

"I didn't order anything else. Maybe the company sent a consolation gift for the long delay," I said.

He got his pocketknife out to cut open the reinforced shipping tape. As he opened the box, an even more incredible gift lay inside with a note from the artist. "The Servant," a painting of Jesus washing an exhausted pastor's feet, stared back at us. The artist had originally painted it to represent a weary Christian businessman but recognized how strongly pastors connected with it. So, he wanted to encourage pastors with this bonus painting.

Tears glistened in Don's eyes. God gave Don precisely the gift he needed, immeasurably more than I could ask or imagine for him. He loved "The Legacy" by Ron DiCianni, a painting of a preacher with images of the prophets and Jesus in the background, which I'd bought for him. But "The Servant" by this same artist meant more to him and arrived when Don planned to resign. I saw his struggle, but God knew better what he needed and when.

The painting I ordered was dear to his heart and hung on his office wall, encouraging him to preach boldly throughout his career as a pastor. The other reminded him how much Jesus loved him and wanted him to continue glorifying God in his work. God showed me that Christmas doesn't always come on our assigned holiday. Sometimes Christmas comes differently than we expect and in his perfect time.

Not Home for the Holidays

Robyn Mulder

CHRISTMAS WAS NOT GOING TO be the same this year. For the first time ever, I would be away from my family over the holidays. I wouldn't even be with my host family in Madrid, Spain. They had decided to travel to the northwest corner of the country to visit my host mom's family in Galicia.

When they had first talked about it, all of us were going to go, but as the holidays approached, plans changed. As a shy twenty-year-old, I couldn't help but assume that they just wanted a break from their timid houseguest. I felt rejected, but I was also a bit relieved that I wouldn't have to go and meet more family members and try to converse with them in Spanish. My knowledge of the language was good, but I was too self-conscious to be myself and talk freely with people. Who was I kidding? I had that problem in English too!

This Christmas was going to be *terrible* (yes, it's the same word in Spanish and English) if I couldn't find a way to get through my home-sickness and fix my negative mindset.

First Semester Jitters

I grew up in a suburb of Grand Rapids, Michigan, with my parents and two younger sisters. I was a quiet kid when I wasn't around my family, and I'm sure I shocked everyone when I decided to attend college seven hundred miles away in Orange City, Iowa. Northwestern College was just the place for me as I made friends and studied Spanish. For my major, I had to spend at least a semester abroad. I chose the program in Spain, and I decided to go for my entire junior year.

> It was exciting to think about, but once I got there, I was terrified.

It was exciting to think about, but once I got there, I was terrified. I rode the bus from the airport with other students in our program. Once we got to downtown Madrid, the rest of the students had to make their way to their host families on their own. Luckily, the program director had to take me to the place where I was staying because she wasn't sure the host family was ready for me. They were doing some renovations in their fifth-floor apartment. I heaved a sigh of relief and followed her to their door.

Once I got there, I settled in with my new host parents and their two-year-old son, Jesusete. He was cute, but he could also be very naughty. I'd never had a little brother before, so it was fun to play with him—most of the time. There's nothing more humbling than to be corrected by a toddler. One day when we were eating breakfast, I couldn't come up with the word for "spoon." I knew it, but I drew a total blank. Jesusete eyed me with disdain and enunciated his assistance. "Es una *cuchara*," he slowly told me, surely baffled that someone my age didn't know the name of a common utensil.

Other things were a challenge too. My first attempt to ride a city bus ended with me going back up to the apartment and telling my host dad that I had decided not to go (instead of admitting that I was too nervous to get on). I later got more comfortable with public transportation, and I took buses all over the city. The first time I rode the subway wasn't quite as bad. I was nervous, but I had a Spanish friend with me, and he showed me how it worked. Later, he called me the "reina del metro" ("queen of the subway") because I took it everywhere as I explored Madrid.

I had a hard time speaking enough in my language classes. I would often say, "Soy tímida" (I'm shy). One of my teachers finally called my bluff. "I don't think Robyn is shy," she said (in Spanish) one day. I was so insulted, but she was probably right. I wasn't truly shy. I just wanted to say things perfectly, so I felt nervous about what came out of my mouth. Once I felt more comfortable, I could speak more.

I wanted to find a church, but most of them were Catholic. I was too scared to visit Protestant churches at first, but as I got used to my new home, I started checking out different places. One Sunday, I tried a small church on the north side of Madrid, about a half hour away by subway.

> Those friends turned out to be a big part of how I survived that Christmas away from my family.

I knew right away that I had found my church home. The people were nice. The pastor was an American missionary with a family. The youth group welcomed me and made me feel like I belonged, even though I was a little older than most of them, and I still didn't talk much. They patiently asked me questions and helped me improve my Spanish. Those friends turned out to be a big part of how I survived that Christmas away from my family.

Would Christmas Vacation Break Me?

Back in 1986, we didn't have cell phones. Phone calls between the U.S. and Spain were expensive. I talked to my family once in a while, but not nearly as often as I would have liked. I wrote letters to them, and they sent some to me, but I definitely felt alone as I approached the holidays.

My host family was heading off to Galicia without me, and I was being shipped off to another house while they were gone. Well, it was only about a mile away, but it felt like I was starting over when I moved in with my friend Teresa's host mom. She was nice, but it was hard to adjust to a new personality and schedule. My friend wasn't even going to be there for Christmas because she had already moved to Seville for her second-semester studies.

During my college years, I had started having some bouts of depression, and this situation proved to be one of those challenging times. I was homesick, stressed about my new home situation, and not sure how I was going to get through Christmas without my family.

Three Things Redeemed Christmas for Me

Christmas vacation could have been absolutely *terrible*, but I made it through, thanks to a few fortunate situations.

A box arrived one day, and it was from my grandma. She had taken the time to send my Christmas gifts to me in Madrid. She always seemed to know just what to get all of us kids for Christmas, and she did a great job this time too. New pajamas, a pair of white angel figurines, and several other gifts were all individually wrapped. I was so touched that I cried as I opened each of them. A connection to family! It was just what I needed.

> Christmas vacation could have been absolutely *terrible*, but I made it through.

During our Christmas break, I went on a trip with the youth group from church. We took a bus to a retreat center and spent a couple of days hiking, studying the Bible, singing, eating, and having fun. It was just the distraction I needed so I wasn't thinking as much about missing my family at home in Michigan.

Toward the end of Christmas vacation, I got to go to the airport with our program director and pick up one of my best friends from college. She had spent her first semester in Paris, and now she would be studying in Madrid with me. It was so good to reconnect with a good friend and look forward to the adventures we would have during our second semester.

Just Like That, It Was Over

Like so many situations in life, my Christmas vacation that year was full of ups and downs. I remember the good events that happened during that break, and I remember feeling depressed leading up to Christmas, but I have to admit that most of my memories of that time have faded. I can't remember spending Christmas Day with my temporary host mom, although I'm sure we did something together. I can't remember talking to my family back in Michigan on the phone, but we probably made sure to call on that special day.

I do remember what made that Christmas memorable: gifts from Grandma, time with church friends, and picking up Faith. All of those people turned my Christmas from "terrible" to "unforgettable" (*inolvidable* in Spanish).

I've never had to spend another Christmas away from my family, but I know that *people* are still the ones who can help us through the most difficult seasons of life. We can make it if we have support from family and friends, especially the ones who remind us that Jesus—the baby we celebrate at Christmas—is our greatest source of love and support. Trusting him, we can get through anything we face in life. Even if we're not home for the holidays.

The Fright Before Christmas

Michelle Rayburn

'Twas the night before Christmas, and all through the home,
Most everyone slept, and Mom was alone.
She'd just wrapped the gifts, put them under the tree.
Then she sat by the fire for a moment or three.

She sipped her hot cocoa, and sniffed the pine air,
And soon she had drifted to sleep in her chair.
She dreamed about presents and goodies and toys,
The delight on sweet faces of her girls and boys.

When all of a sudden, she heard a door creak,
As if someone or something were trying to sneak.
Increasing her sense of the impending doom,
She noted four burglars creep into the room.

The bandits snuck over and crouched by the tree,
Mom still as a statue and stifling a scream.
Each picked up a present and made for the door,
And quick as a flash they were all back for more.

Mom fretted and worried, "What shall I do?"
And then she remembered, *Hey, I know Kung Fu!*
She sprang from the chair and tackled the first,
Surprising those thieves with her hasty outburst.

With a chop to one thief and a kick to another,
She leveled two robbers, that sweet little mother.
Then with a brave leap—Jackie Chan would approve—
She took out two more with one swift, graceful move.

Four robbers, one momma who knew her Kung Fu.
She pointed her finger and lectured the crew,
"You bring back those toys and then get out of here,
For Christmas is all about love and good cheer."

They scurried away, gave up on their crime,
And now we are just about done with this rhyme.
But first, about Momma, who never did scream,
Her fright before Christmas was only a dream.

For fun, use this as a ready-made drama for a group, pulling impromptu volunteers from the audience. The narrator reads aloud, and volunteers act out the drama. Entertaining for both adults and children! You'll need 1 narrator, 1 momma, and 4 robbers. (You may have to issue caution with the acting out, lest volunteers get too exuberant in their roles.)

A Medley of Memories

Sally Ferguson

WHEN I THINK OF HOME, I reminisce about Christmas Eve. My children were wrapped up in their new Christmas pajamas, surely dreaming of festive packages. When Hubby came home after midnight from the Christmas Eve service at church, we giddily brought the presents out of their hiding places to prepare for the morrow's unwrapping. He made bridges and tunnels for the train around the tree by strategically positioning packages. The tree lights twinkled, adding to our merriment. And I felt peace envelop my heart as a contented anticipation settled into the night.

One of my favorite memories from my growing-up years was a wintery December when a friend's family came caroling. We welcomed them into the warmth of home as they shed coats, mittens, and hats. Mom pulled out her mixer and ingredients to make homemade eggnog, then loaded platters with Christmas cookies. It was a wonderful celebration of hospitality and friendship as we cradled our cup of Christmas cheer. I'd hoped to replicate that scene in my own home one day.

Blue Christmas

Home hasn't always been the place of secure and happy Christmas memories. There have been times I felt homeless—my mom's sudden death, my grandmother's passing sixteen months later, my father-in-law's surprising death from COVID-19, and my mother-in-law's demise six weeks following. The loss of these prayer warriors was a great blow to my sense of stability. They gave me moorings of home and heart. In truth, they were passing the baton to the next generation. It became our turn to model the hospitality of home and unconditional love of family. The bereft ache morphed into a matriarchal sense of calling and commitment to create a nest for my own to flock to for shelter.

> The hard part about losing your moorings is the restlessness that threatens your peace.

The hard part about losing your moorings is the restlessness that threatens your peace. When there is a disconnect from relationships, there is also a lost connection in your sense of self. It happened my junior year in college. I spent the sultry summer with missionaries in Egypt, learning about the ancient culture and making friends along the way. At home, I had been fighting for my independence and was glad to put some distance between my parents and me. I found out, instead, your troubles go with you, even around the world. It was an important lesson in the value of family relationships and determining to resolve conflict rather than run from it. I found out peace on earth had to begin with me.

It Came Upon a Midnight Clear

While still a student, one evening under a tree on my college campus, I cried out to God, asking about my life's purpose. I felt him direct my eyes to the massive branches stretching out above and knew I had a legacy of faith to pass to others. Just as those branches swept toward each other, my future connections would need support and encouragement on their faith journey.

I had a task to cling to. I had a future to embrace. God's transformative power gave me hope and a desire to persevere. And later, I realized that a legacy of faith had to start at home, with family.

All I Want for Christmas Is You

My sister's first trip to our home in Western New York came the Christmas following her husband's death. His health had precluded traveling from Indiana, and her visit marked a new era in the logistics of where we gathered as a family. It was a starry night where you could see your breath scurry across the frigid air. She carried boxes of presents into the living room, where wood crackled in the fireplace and carols played in the background. We celebrated with great fanfare.

She had come home where family could embrace her. We had come full circle in our relationship of sisterhood, now friends in the trenches of life.

Mary, Did You Know?

One of the sweetest memories of family was the anticipation of a baby due on Christmas Eve. I was looking forward to creating our own traditions and thought often of the similarities between the phases of Mary's pregnancy and my own. What was it like to await the arrival of the Savior and to make a home that now included the One who was there in the beginning? What was it like to hold his tiny face in your hands and see your own reflected there? How would it feel to see the Father in his eyes when he called you Mother? I felt a special kinship with this young mom from long ago and longed to create a home filled with love.

What makes a house a home? How does love thrive there? Glossy magazines, elaborate books, and an unlimited number of websites are dedicated to seeking out the elusive definition of home. Colleges try to capture that feeling with homecoming and class reunions. Churches celebrate anniversaries and milestones. And families commemorate heritage and legacies.

At one of our family reunions, a young cousin kayaked around Lake Junaluska with Hubby and me. Splashing our oars, conversing across the ripples, and stretching our muscles together became a connection to recall many years later. His enthusiasm for life infected us with hope for the next generation and kindled a yearning to gather our kin repeatedly.

In the same way, a family that comes together in a time of crisis builds community within itself. Memories are made from shared experiences and bond one another together. Caring for loved ones in their last days increases fondness and attachment to each other. We found new footing in relating to each other as we sought the best for the parents we all loved so well. We found out we could do the hard work of physical care and financial decisions.

We rose to the challenge of giving them home and giving of ourselves. We grew in our confidence in what God equips us to do when we think we can't. We're stronger. And we have a new appreciation for the conviction required for preserving hearth and home throughout the generations.

I'll Be Home for Christmas

My Dad's favorite Christmas song is "I'll Be Home for Christmas." His tour of service in the Korean War fostered such a profound homesickness that he still tears up when he hears the melody. In my years of wandering overseas and cross country, my travels also enriched my thoughts of home. Home's cozy surroundings gave me a sense of familiar security, but even more so, close proximity to family gave it that personal touch.

I see it in my grandchildren's eyes as they burst through the door, looking for hugs from Grandma. I hear it in my husband's voice when he calls out "hello" upon returning from work. I taste it in the salty tears of life's struggles. And I feel it in my heart when I settle in with my Lord.

His gentle reminder brings to mind the many ways he's been there for me, even as my own memory recedes. I remember he knocks at the door and sits with me when I wrestle with the uncertainties of life. I ponder the enthrallment of my eternal home with him in heaven. And I wonder if maybe I have come home for the holidays too. My wanderings have ceased, and my heart settles into God's arms for safe harbor once more. I know it will be the best Christmas ever when I come home for Christmas.

Operation Christmas Rescue

Charlaine Martin

"U H-OH!" MY HUSBAND AND I chorused. Our son hit a meltdown when he unwrapped his Christmas present. He had just opened the package to find G.I. Joe's leg lying loose in the box. Was it a casualty of war? Nope. But what really happened? We weren't sure for the moment.

"I didn't break it!" Seth howled, hopped up, and ran over to hand his dad the box with the action figure.

For once, his meltdown was legitimate. Don examined it while our eight-year-old son sniveled, hopeful Dad could fix it. Don picked up the leg separate from the rest of the action figure while I looked over his shoulder. At first, we were skeptical, but as we checked it out, we could see Seth couldn't have broken it. The hip connection was shattered, with the rest of G.I. Joe still strapped down in the factory packaging.

His six-year-old sister, Paige,* trotted over to Seth and hugged him, holding her new doll. "It's okay. Daddy can fix it." She tried her best to console him.

Miffy, our three-year-old, sat with her gifts and glanced in Seth's direction, concern in her eyes.

"Seth," Don looked him in the eye with compassion in his voice, "We'll have to take it back to the store and see if we can get another one tomorrow. We see that you didn't break it." He patted our disappointed son on the shoulder.

Sitting beside Don on the sofa, I hugged Seth, affirming his dad's promise, "We will exchange it for another one in the morning." Seth nodded his head, his pouty face tear-streaked.

The Challenge of Showing Grace

Our gangly whirlwind, fueled by his attention deficit disorder with hyperactivity (ADHD), often let Seth's relentless curiosity about how things were made take over. His infinite imagination, complete with sound effects, made his make-believe scenes come to life. Because of these two traits, he often broke things—primarily his birthday and Christmas gifts.

> His infinite imagination, complete with sound effects, made his make-believe scenes come to life.

Parenting a child on the autism spectrum presented unique challenges. It wasn't just the presents he damaged. A few shower curtain rods fell victim to Seth's imaginary superhero pursuits. At the same time, Paige became his unwitting victim as an "arch villain" as she sat watching *My Little Pony* cartoons with Miffy. It was hard to feel sympathy for him when he broke his toys, had to give over his piggy bank to our landlord (my desperate solution to curb his behavior issues), or howled in pain when Paige bit his arm when he least suspected her revenge.

Our family life was never dull. As a result, Don and I felt frazzled from all of his antics. It would have been easy to chalk up his broken G.I. Joe that Christmas as a casualty of his inquisitive mind rather than recognize that it wasn't his fault *this* time.

Following Through with Grace

That year was a big deal for boys ages five to twelve who wanted G.I. Joe collectible action figures for Christmas. Seth and his friend agreed they wanted this special edition GI Joe with light and sound weapons, which drew Seth's attention like a magnet. We usually couldn't afford the popular toys, but an unexpected Christmas bonus made it possible. However, its popularity made them scarce.

On our anniversary, we ate out at a nice restaurant and did our Christmas shopping afterward. We liked going to our local discount store to put our kids' Christmas presents in layaway. Since Seth and Paige—and Miffy tagging along—loved to snoop in our closet and other hiding places to find out what we got them, layaway helped us make their gifts a delightful surprise.

> We couldn't wait to see his face on Christmas morning!

That evening, we were fortunate to score one, but the one Seth wanted was sold out. He would still be thrilled to get one, even if it wasn't the exact action figure he wanted. At least the boys' soldiers could be buddies instead of twins.

Excited that we'd scored a coveted G.I. Joe that Seth wanted, we couldn't wait to see his face on Christmas morning!

Grace Fixed What Mattered Most

Much to our dismay, Seth's wasn't the smile with a shriek of delight we had hoped for. We felt terrible that this incident happened to that special present.

Our son's fragile self-image was at risk. So, we got up early the morning after Christmas and dropped our kids off at a friend's house. Once we pulled into the parking lot, we hurried inside and stood in the store's hour-long return line, snaking through the makeshift cueing maze. When it was our turn, we stepped up to the returns counter.

The store associate looked over the G.I. Joe and then at us. "It was broken in the package," my husband explained to her as he pointed out the factory bands holding G.I. Joe firmly in the box.

Glancing at him through her glasses, expressing her disbelief with the tilt of her head and raised eyebrows, she typed information into the register. She handed the total in cash to him, and we embarked on a speedy hunt for another. As we picked through the boxes on the shelf, we discovered there were none to be found. So we hopped into our car and drove to a popular toy store nearby.

Viola! We found them, but not the same one we had given him. It was still from the collector's series, though. It looked cool, so we paid for it and took it home.

Now we had the smile with squeals of delight that make Christmas so enjoyable! His face lit up as he begged his dad to take it out of the box for him, clearly afraid that he might accidentally break it. He hugged us both and dashed off with it to play. Paige and Miffy skittered behind him, offering to bring their Barbie and doll to play too.

When Seth broke toys in the past, we'd never tried to replace what he'd broken. He needed to learn to handle his things better. Often, we mended them with super glue, paper clips, duct tape, and anything else that might do the job. But they didn't work quite the way the manufacturer intended. A handful of them met their fate in the trash can. This time, we felt it most important to mend his broken heart and spare his little boy's self-image. He needed our compassion, not our disapproval. Besides, *he* hadn't broken it this time.

Grace Comes Full Circle

Now on the edge of turning forty with three children of his own, Seth is currently on the giving end of showing grace to his neurodiverse prodigies. Seeing him emulate this parental love and understanding warms my heart.

Recently, Seth shared his inside scoop of that particular Christmas with me when we discussed it on the phone. Tears filled my eyes as I heard what our unexpected grace meant to him. While making dinner for his family, he assured me, "Mom, I was always happy with most of the toys I received, but those in the latest commercials were dream stuff. I didn't expect to get them. My ADHD attention craved stimulation from the special effects of that G.I. Joe line, so when I opened my gift, I was thrilled when I saw what you and Dad gave me!"

> Seeing him emulate this parental love and understanding warms my heart.

"Seth," I replied, resting my arm on our dining table after my meal. "I'm sure you realize now that we couldn't afford the popular Christmas toys in the commercials, but their popularity also made them scarce. However, with your dad's bonus that year, we couldn't resist making your Christmas wish happen."

I was surprised to learn that the replacement we found the day after Christmas didn't have the special effects. Sitting back in my chair, I apologized, "Gee, Seth, I'm sorry. We were just so focused on hunting down that series."

Encouraging me, he said, "No worries! I was thrilled you'd go to the trouble to replace it. That's what made it even more special."

Here's what really tugged at my heart yet confirmed we did the right thing. Seth continued, "If you hadn't trusted me when I said I didn't break it, I didn't think you'd ever believe me or trust me again with such a nice toy."

In the background, I heard a commotion. "Michael!" Seth called out his son for doing something he shouldn't.

I chuckled, "God blessed you with children just like yourself!"

With a sigh, he snickered, "Yep!"

I feel blessed to see him show his children the same parental love. He doesn't let them off the hook for inappropriate behavior. Still, I also see him extend unexpected grace when his children desperately need it. It makes me feel like we did something right when I had made so many mistakes during his childhood. I didn't understand then that his disorder was a gift from God.

Our compassion for Seth wasn't lost on our daughters either. I found it interesting how Paige and Miffy learned to care for their brother's plights, sometimes standing in the gap for him at school over the years. Unexpected grace had a ripple effect.

As his mom, I received his unexpected grace by learning how our decision to replace the G.I. Joe for him was a gift of protecting his priceless self-worth. His words warmed my heart and made me cry. The gift Seth returned to me through his version of the story restored my value as a parent who grew up in a family where grace wasn't often shown. Grace came around full circle for both of us.

*Paige, Miffy, and Michael are names changed for privacy.

Christmas Is for Relationships

Pam Farrel

Center your heart on the deeper meaning of the holidays. This will help everyone become easier to get along with because the heart of the holiday will remain intact.

Hear what your friends and family are voicing as their stress and listen carefully to them—this is a gift that will lower their stress.

Reach out as a family to help others in order to keep the proper perspective on what is really important in life.

Invest in memories, not material goods. Make time for family baking, caroling, tree decorating, or board games.

Speak your love in words. The best gift you can give is for a person to hear their value and worth from your lips.

Take time for romance. The greatest gift you can give your children is a happy marriage.

Make time to reach out to extended family. In-person is best. However, a visit via Zoom or a phone call to grandparents, aunts, and uncles will brighten their holidays.

Assume nothing. Ask those who are celebrating with you what their expectations are and communicate the plan clearly so people feel informed and valued.

Stay flexible. Don't be a Christmas boss, ordering family around. Instead, slow the pace, gather consensus, and give options so that you create an environment of connecting and sharing.[4]

Faith
and Hope

A Grinch-Proof Christmas

Michelle Rayburn

'D FALLEN ASLEEP IN THE recliner, my crochet hook and yarn in hand—again. So many homemade gifts to finish, and there wasn't enough time in a day to complete the Christmas gifts for everyone on my list.

Between running kids to practices, staying on top of my schedule of twenty-plus piano students coming and going from our home all week, and volunteering at church, time had a way of disappearing faster than a plate of fresh chocolate chip cookies around teenage boys.

So, I started bringing projects with me when I ran errands. My crochet tote bag was the most portable and contained the easiest projects to pick up whenever I had a few extra minutes to wait somewhere. One of those occasions came when I had forty minutes between dropping off my son and the start of his basketball game.

I found a spot up in the bleachers and pulled out my yarn. Other parents trickled in during the warmup, but I didn't really notice the spots filling in around me.

"You're too young for crochet." The voice startled me.

Is this a citation for acts of public crochet? And how does he know it's crochet, not knitting? I'm not sure how the man discovered this supposed age rule about the handicraft. I'd lived more than forty years without ever hearing such a thing. "I've been crocheting since I was twelve."

"Well then! You're too young to be bringing it out in public. It's something to do at home. And old ladies make a lot of useless stuff and doilies."

He had a point there about useless stuff. Put "granny square shorts" into a Pinterest search, and you'll see the logic. However, I am not an old lady. So, point overruled by his own accusation about my youthfulness.

The pace at which I hooked and looped yarn accelerated. I yanked up another length of string from the ball in my tote and kindly explained that my hats and slippers would *not* be useless gifts. I wasn't feeling overwhelming Christmas kindness in my heart toward Mr. Grinch just then.

"Bringing it out in public." What in the world? I shook my head and carried on with my should-have-been-clandestine task of creating "useless" stuff.

I'd let what was most likely lighthearted—done in true northern Wisconsin style—teasing from Mr. Grinch get to my head. Ope. Dat's where I went wrong. Insert strong nasal tone here.

Other people sew tags into their homemade Christmas gifts saying things like "Made with love by Michelle." I'd have to look for some "Made with sarcasm and defiance" tags for my projects.

Perhaps he wasn't the Grinch after all. Maybe it was me.

My Tendency to Go Overboard

I've nearly ruined a few Christmases with my obsession with being a poster child for time-consuming and useless activities. And if someone even hinted at the idea that my activities were unnecessary, I had a comeback ready. It. Was. *Christmas.*

There was the year I hand-stamped rolls of brown craft paper for all the gift wrapping. Do you know how long it takes to cover a giant sheet of paper with rubber stamps and ink, only to do it all over again for the next gift? Then I added plaid fabric bows and hot-glued sprigs of dried berries, silk flowers, and fake evergreens to the wrapped gifts. And I made special gift tags. Our children couldn't use the ping-pong table for weeks because it was my gift-wrapping station. I was saving money, you know. Or was I?

That paper came off those boxes and was crumpled into a trash bag lickety-split at the family gathering. You know, the kind where "Santa," aka Grandpa, hands out one gift with a pledge that we will all watch each other open our gifts. And then, by gift number four, mass chaos ensues, and there is a flurry of ripping and thanking and tossing. And then it's done. In three minutes, weeks of painstaking precision stuffed into a trash bag. Within the hour, Santa-Grandpa, will take that bag out to the burn barrel and incinerate the remnants of unwrapping.

Don't you care about how much time I spent wrapping your gifts? Don't you see how pretty and oh-so-Martha-Stewart-inspired they are? No. They didn't.

And what I didn't realize yet was that those things didn't make it Christmas. And they certainly didn't save me money. A jumbo roll of Christmas wrap sold for a few dollars on Christmas clearance, and I soon learned to pick up several to store for the next year. And when gift bags came around, that was even better. I could finish my wrapping in fifteen minutes if I pulled out the plastic tote of multi-reused bags, put everything into something relatively close to size, and slapped a sticky note onto it with a name.

> Like the real Mr. Grinch of Seuss fame, my heart had been a few sizes too small.

Like the real Mr. Grinch of Seuss fame, my heart had been a few sizes too small. I wanted to hear people ooh and ahh over my handmade things and beautifully wrapped gifts, but I didn't see how much time that process stole from my family, how much energy it used, and how much it stole away from the purpose for the season.

In the famed fable, the Grinch stole every present. Every toy. Every Christmas tree. Even the logs for the fire. But the result wasn't what he expected.

As children awoke to discover what he'd done, their response was merry singing. "It came without ribbons! It came without tags! It came without packages, boxes or bags! . . . What if Christmas . . . perhaps . . . means a little bit more."[5]

My Not-To-Do List

My Christmases have grown simpler over the years. There are many things I once did that I no longer do. My not-to-do list is now bigger than my to-do list.

Do not get out totes and totes of artificial pine, lights, bows, beads, and boards. Check. I sorted and tossed and whittled it down to a couple of totes of tree ornaments and decorations, most of which stay in the boxes every year.

Do not spend more than one hour setting up the Christmas tree. Check. Maybe it's two. But the ornaments are simple. One year, I didn't get around to putting them on, so I enjoyed a tree with lights and the ribbon garland—that's as far as I'd got. Another year, I skipped the tree and put fairy lights and mini-ornaments on a two-foot Norway pine.

Do not put any decorations outside. Check. Wisconsin. Remember? No one, and I mean no one, wants to take those down in January when it's forty below zero. And lights pose a problem when icicles and ice dams take over the roof.

Do not bake trays and trays of cookies and goodies. Check. I seldom do any Christmas baking anymore. My mom always does. And she shares. I eat gluten-free, anyway.

> I have found sweet freedom in going only to the things that really matter to me.

Do not go to every party or event. Check. I have found sweet freedom in going only to the things that really matter to me. Not every concert or party needs my presence.

Do not make homemade gifts unless they have true meaning for the recipient. Check. Most of the people I know don't need another one of my canning jar candles or snowman-painted recycled lightbulb ornaments. Cute? Yes. But I'm fine with only doing what I want to do. And helping others declutter is a gift too, right?

Do not shop. Check. I hardly do! We don't exchange with our siblings. And instead of shopping for our children and grandchildren, I now get one small thing for each grandchild to open at Christmas. And then I book a getaway for all of us instead. That time spent at a resort or Airbnb each spring is a fun way of creating memories together.

My Must-Do List

One of the best ways to Grinch-proof Christmas is to change my focus to what really matters. I can celebrate Christmas without a tree. I don't need cookies, or poinsettias, or strings of lights. I don't even need Christmas music or Hallmark movies. **Gasp**

My to-do list includes remembering Jesus. He is Immanuel, God with us. "So the Word became human and made his home among us. He was full of unfailing love and faithfulness. And we have seen his gory, the glory of the Father's one and only Son" (John 1:14).

> Nothing grows my too-small heart like having Jesus here, dwelling.

Nothing grows my too-small heart like having Jesus here, dwelling. Loving. Living. His presence the only present. Not one that can be gift-wrapped with a bow or overdecorated. But one I might easily overlook when I'm caught up in the frenzy of gifts and decorations and lights. His timeless love forever dwells among us, illuminating our hearts with his eternal light. So, I ask myself, when I'm pondering a throwback to my homespun and overdone days, *What if Christmas, perhaps, means a little bit more? And what if less is always more?*

Jakey's Christmas Stocking

Kristine Zimmer Orkin

R EADY TO GO CHRISTMAS SHOPPING?" I asked my just-turned-four-year-old son. All business, Joey picked up his little coin purse filled with pennies. Inside his mitten, he held a list of presents he wanted to buy, all of them jotted down in his squiggly four-year-old handwriting. A secret coded script that only he could decipher.

He lifted his mittened hand and jangled his treasure pouch. "Ready," he replied. With a hasty goodbye peck on his dad's cheek, Joey marched out the front door to our waiting car. "Let's go," he called back to me. Time was a-wasting, and he had a mission to accomplish.

Ten minutes later, we arrived at Joey's favorite holiday place, the "Christmas Store," as he'd dubbed it two years prior upon his first visit. His toddler eyes had been aglow with the glittery magic of lighted trees, frosty snowmen, and moving electric toys throughout the large room. His head and shoulders rocked back and forth, neck craning to follow pointy-eared elves—dressed in festive red and green outfits with curly-toed shoes and a jingle-bell cap—as they worked the store, assisting customers and entertaining awestruck children.

On that first visit, we'd seated Joey in a shopping cart and pushed our way through the aisles, tossing in boxes of tree lights, ornaments, and small gifts. Our purchases went unnoticed by our little guy who was so intensely engaged with the sights and sounds of his surroundings. Eyes wide and unblinking, he pointed continuously at anything that caught his attention. His quick intakes of breath and gurgly "oohs" were mixed with high-pitched giggles and hand clapping.

Every year since then, the Christmas Store has claimed top spot on our shopping priority list. Today we had a special item in mind.

> Every year since then, the Christmas Store has claimed top spot on our shopping priority list. Today we had a special item in mind.

"Mama, look over there." Joey squealed with delight and ran toward the display of stockings hanging along the far wall.

Dozens of cute, colorful children's Christmas stockings hung in the lowest two rows of the display, with adult stockings above them. Large, netted stockings filled with various candies were meant for Saint Nicholas Day. Either Joey hadn't seen those temptations, or he was absorbed in his own purpose.

Meticulously examining the many offerings before him, he resorted to automatically answering my questions without once looking up from his work.

"Hmm. This is a pretty one, don't you think?" I attempted conversation, holding up a small, baby-sized sock.

"Nah." He didn't even glance at my suggestion.

"How about this blue one with the snowman?"

"No, it's gotta be red for Christmas." He dug through piles of stockings lying neatly on shelves, tossing unacceptable ones to the side. So much for the careful display laid out by some hard-working employee.

His gaze roamed the entire length of the wall section. Back-and-forth a second time, and a third. He stopped. His body stilled for a mere second, and then he took off running. I half-heartedly reassembled the pile of my son's rejects before hurrying to catch up with him.

Red furry stocking with white trim. Joey caressed the plush fabric. He unhooked the sock from its metal hanger in the wall and rubbed the softness across his cheek. His fingers found the toy bear sticking out of a pocket in the stocking, and he lifted it out. Attached by a thick cord of thread, the bear's body hung freely outside the pocket.

My little boy stood silently, turning the stocking over and over in his hands, deep in thought. I watched him in fascination, oblivious to the Christmas music and the shoppers around us. I never heard the saleslady approach until she spoke.

"Is that stocking for you?" she asked Joey, kneeling to make eye contact with him.

He broke his concentration to look at her. "No," he said. "It's for my baby brother."

The kind lady smiled and further engaged him. "Oh, you have a little brother! That's pretty exciting."

"He's dead." Joey turned back to his examination.

I heard a loud gasp. I wasn't sure if it came from the saleslady or from me. *He's dead.* A flat statement of fact, spoken with the innocent candor only a young child could muster. A bit of information he felt this woman needed to know to fully appreciate the importance of his selecting just the right stocking.

She and I looked at each other, the saleslady still kneeling next to Joey. She rose slowly but stayed by my side, neither of us knowing what to say.

I broke the silence. "Our baby boy was stillborn last month." Tears welled in my eyes as I said the words.

She squeezed my arm, then gave me a hug. "I'm so sorry," she whispered.

"I like this one, Mama. This is Jakey's stocking." Joey's voice broke the tense moment. "See, it has a pocket for M&Ms or a candy cane. Maybe Santa Claus will put a little toy in there as a surprise. And the bear, see how . . ." He looked up at me, smiling, excited, and kept talking.

The woman left us to our mother-son deliberation. I don't think Joey noticed her walk away.

After another few minutes of listening to him tout the specialness of this stocking over all others, and me obligingly fawning over his perfect choice, Joey and I finally made our significant purchase and hurried home to show Daddy.

Earlier in the week, the three of us had gone through the annual rituals of past family Christmases. Happier Christmases. We frosted cookies and loaded them with holiday sprinkles. Daddy and Joey erected a lopsided gingerbread house with noticeable little nibbles along the edges. Nat King Cole sang as we hung wreath swags and set out candles everywhere, while ornamental angels brought good tidings to every room in our home. A lighted Christmas village sprawled across the big table in our living room. We had painted Merry Christmas on the front window and unwrapped the nativity set. Joey carefully placed each statue in and around the stable. He held the baby Jesus with reverence and set the manger strategically in the middle of the scene.

Daddy put the heavy stocking holders on the mantel, and we each hung our stocking. As we admired our work, Joey burst into tears.

"What's wrong?" we asked.

In a heartbroken lament, our little boy had looked at us. "Jakey doesn't have a stocking."

> It took this young child to enlighten us that life had, indeed, changed and would never be quite the same as before.

An oversight of the highest magnitude. Joey's dad and I had been dealing privately with our grief over baby Jacob, trying to keep life happy and normal for Joey. It took this young child to enlighten us that life had, indeed, changed and would never be quite the same as before. That "normal" wasn't normal if you didn't include *every* family member.

He had a brother. Jakey was part of our family and shouldn't—couldn't—be overlooked. Our mantel didn't accurately display the family Orkin. Someone important was missing. His brother needed a stocking.

We planned a shopping trip to repair the situation. Joey insisted on choosing his brother's stocking himself. He needed to be sure the task was done properly.

Today, that task had been achieved and with great respect. Tonight, Daddy set another cast-iron holder on the mantel, and we hung the fourth stocking. Joey carefully hung his brother's next to his. With great pride, he stepped back and approved the mantel, finally complete and representing us all. He looked heavenward.

"Hey, Jakey. That's *your* stocking." He pointed to the furry red sock with white trim, the pocket for M&Ms, and a toy bear hanging from the front. "I picked it out just for you."

Then, Joey kissed his palm and blew toward the sky, sending kisses to his baby brother in heaven.

Christmas Came Anyway

Pam Halter

MOMMY, WHEN ARE WE GONNA get the tree out and set it up?" my daughter Mary asked.

Never, I thought. But how could I say that to an excited eleven-year-old with big blue eyes and the world's most beautiful smile? So, I mumbled, "Soon." However, having an autistic teenage daughter, Anna, with an uncontrolled seizure disorder consumed my thoughts. Anxiety and depression were my constant companions.

Soon came rather quickly, and there was my husband, bringing our artificial tree in from the garage. Mary put on Christmas music, and the setting up of the tree commenced.

We quickly found out that this year's tree decorating was not going to be the same as all the other years. Our two young cats, Hemmy, gray with black stripes, and Dusty, light tan with tan stripes, became very interested in what we were doing. They explored the box and nibbled on the branches, played and rolled underneath, and generally got in the way.

Once the tree was up, and as we started to untangle the lights, Hemmy climbed the tree and wouldn't let Dusty up. He whapped Dusty on the head as if to say, "This is my tree! No trespassing!"

We laughed at their antics (even me!) for a while before we realized Hemmy wouldn't allow lights on the tree either.

Or garland.

Or ornaments.

My husband said, "We'll give him a while, and when he gets tired of it, we'll finish decorating the tree."

Laughter Mingles with Grief

The tree never got decorated, except for one gray-with-black-stripes cat. Dusty eventually got in the lower part of the tree branches, and they batted at each other, played, and even took naps while in the tree. They only took it down twice.

> The tree never got decorated, except for one gray-with-black-stripes cat.

While I laughed at the cats in the tree, my heart still wept. Proverbs 14:13 says, "Laughter can conceal a heavy heart, but when the laughter ends, the grief remains." Most people with depression conceal it with laughter or maybe just a smile. When it progresses, like mine did, we pull back from things that used to give us joy.

I didn't have the energy to decorate the house either, so we prepared for the season with very little glitz and glamour. Hemmy and Dusty kept us entertained as they enjoyed our tree, and we got used to an unlit Christmas tree with a gray-striped cat "decoration" near the top and a tan cat "decoration" near the bottom. We called it our wildlife-themed tree.

My parents came to stay with us, as they had been doing for a few years, for Christmas Eve, Christmas Day, and the day after Christmas. Then they drove down to my brother's house in North Carolina to spend a few days with his family before they went on to Florida to spend the winter.

I sat in church on Christmas Eve, wondering why I even bothered. I tried to sing the carols, but when the opening music for "Joy to the

World" started, I stood with my hymnal clutched to my chest, tears running down my cheeks.

Christmas Comes Anyway

As we drove back, I looked at all the beautifully decorated homes. My heart sank. And guilt followed. I *should* have gotten myself together and put up a few decorations.

But I was so depressed, so exhausted, the guilt didn't even bother me. Much.

Okay, it did. It bothered me because I worried what my children—or even my neighbors—would think. But they didn't seem to notice. The cats in the tree held most of their attention.

"You know, I never did decorate anything," I commented to my mom as we rode.

She smiled and said, "And Christmas came anyway."

Yes, Christmas came anyway. Regardless of my depression, unlit tree, and zero decorations, Christmas came anyway. I pondered that for days. Despite our lack of decorations, it was still Christmas—a celebration of Jesus's birth. Kind of like the first Christmas, which took place in a stable. No tree, no lights, no decorations.

In Dr. Seuss's story, *How The Grinch Stole Christmas*, the Grinch tried to steal Christmas by stealing decorations and presents. But Christmas came anyway.

A Light Shines

I might have thought depression had stolen Christmas from me. And like the story tells us, NO ONE can steal Christmas. It's Christmas because Jesus agreed to become human. Agreed to leave his throne in glory. It's nothing to do with decorations, gifts, cookies, lights, or Santa.

Jesus did all that and more. It was prophesied long before he came: "The people who walk in darkness will see a great light. For those who live in a land of deep darkness, a light will shine. . . . For a child is born to us, a son is given to us. The government will rest on his shoulders. And he will be called: Wonderful Counselor, Mighty God, Everlasting Father, Prince of Peace" (Isaiah 9:2, 6).

I read a blog years later that talked about how choosing joy is not a selfish thing. That when things are heavy in our lives, our hearts can and should be light.

Even a line in "O Holy Night" says, "the weary world rejoices." That's what my heart felt. Weary. Sad. Weeping inside all the time, not even knowing why.

But Christmas is Jesus Emmanuel—God with us. Our hearts can and should be light because his birth changed everything. No matter what's going on, Jesus promised us he has overcome the world. Nothing lasts forever except for his kingdom and his love for us.

Our brokenness is temporary.

Our pain is temporary.

Our tears are temporary.

Our sin is temporary.

The world is temporary.

DEATH is temporary!

When Jesus arrived, an angel visited the shepherds, and "the radiance of the Lord's glory surrounded them. They were terrified, but the angel reassured them. 'Don't be afraid!' he said. 'I bring you good news that will bring great joy to all people. The Savior—yes, the Messiah, the Lord—has been born today in Bethlehem, the city of David!'" (Luke 2:9–11).

As I thought about this, I came to the conclusion that what really needs decorating is our hearts. When we fill our hearts with love, joy, and peace, they shine like the brightest star, and contentment drapes our souls like gold garland.

That means even in depression, our hearts can be light. I went through the motions of "doing Christmas" that year, but my mom's words stayed with me for a long time. Christmas came anyway. As I repeated that to myself, even though I still wept inside, my heart grew a little lighter. That gave me hope to keep going.

I didn't feel happy or carefree. I felt light in the sense that this world is not all there is. We can have hope. God doesn't waste anything. He doesn't leave us to bear our burdens alone. Scripture says we don't grieve as those without hope. It doesn't say we *don't* grieve or get depressed. In fact, it says there's a time for grief—and everything else.

Hope Perseveres

When the Magi came searching for Jesus, they left their homes and families to follow a star. They were excited because they believed the prophecy of the Messiah who would be born in Bethlehem. I read once that it took them about two years to get there. *Two years.* Did they feel depressed or ready to give up at times? Did they lose their hope of finding Jesus? I don't know, but they kept going.

They stopped to ask King Herod where Jesus was because they had seen his star and had come to worship him. After that, they continued their journey, following the star until it stopped in Bethlehem over the place where Jesus was. "When they saw the star, they were filled with joy!" (Matthew 2:10).

> God reminded me that joy doesn't come from our circumstances. It comes directly from him.

Joy in this instance can be more closely translated as they were *ecstatic*. It almost made me laugh. Ecstatic? I could barely smile that year, let alone feel ecstatic. God reminded me that joy doesn't come from our circumstances. It comes directly from him. From knowing how much he loves us. I don't know anyone I'd sacrifice any of my children for, let alone strangers or enemies. But Romans 5:8 says, "God showed his great love for us by sending Christ to die for us while we were still sinners."

That, my friends, is where joy can be found.

Christmas with no decorations. Maybe we should all try it at least once. We may find joy in unexpected places, like in a song, a star in the night sky, or the words of a mother.

I still enjoy the lights, glitz, and glamour, but the lesson of that one Christmas stayed with me. I still struggle with depression and anxiety, but I have a terrific Christian therapist who always points me to Jesus. When I focus on his beautiful face and remember what he did for me, I can celebrate Christmas with a full heart. With or without cookies, gifts, or decorations.

Joy to the world!

Mom's Favorite Ornament

Rosemarie DiCristo

MOM'S FAVORITE CHRISTMAS ORNAMENT WAS my favorite too: a tiny plaster angel with a painted-on golden gown and reddish-brown sprinkled-with-glitter hair.

All of us—me, Mom, Dad, and Josie—wondered why her hair was glitter. Because angels are sparkly beings so naturally, they'd have sparkly hair? Because she's a Christmas ornament, and 90 percent of Christmas ornaments are covered with glitter? Whatever. We just thought she was pretty.

And she was. Until she broke.

Mom and I bought her together when I was seven—at Andy's, a dusty old junk store on Burke Avenue that's stuffed to the rafters with a hodge-podge of things that look as though they've been there since maybe forever. Almost hidden, way back on a shelf, was our angel, wearing a serene yet sassy expression on her face and reaching out plaster arms "that will enfold us with all the love in the world." Mom's words were a whisper, as if talking normally would somehow destroy the aura of magic surrounding the little statue.

Then Mom grinned at me, adding just as softly, "Let's name her 'Ilona,' because that name means 'light,' and angels are beings of light."

I nodded, my voice also feather-delicate. "She's splendiferous. We're gonna buy her, right?"

"Right-o, kiddo!" Mom said with a smile that lit up the sky.

ILONA WAS ALWAYS THE FIRST ornament out of the Christmas trunk and the first decoration we put up before the tree or anything. I was given the honor of placing Ilona on her spot on the mantel because Ilona's an angel and my name's Angela.

But this year, Ilona slipped from my hands and shattered.

"Oh, no," Josie cried.

I just stared at the jagged pieces. Head and shoulders, waist to feet, and the crumbs of one arm scattered on the rock-hard parquet floor.

"Hey, it's not so bad." Dad knelt by the wreckage. "Ilona broke in chunks. She can be glued back together, easy-peasy."

Josie scooped up the pieces as gently as if it were Mom lying there. I watched her cradle Ilona's head and shoulders and waist to feet in her cupped hands. But when she reached for the pile of dust that had been Ilona's left arm, Josie hesitated.

"It's ... We probably can't fix that." Her eyes searched my stiff face, looking for any reaction.

Up until then, I'd been silent. But now my voice screeched, "Probably can't? Probably? Try definitely can't, Josie. As in, not ever."

"Angela ..." Dad's voice was soft as he reached out to bear-hug me.

I twisted away. "No. Ilona can't be fixed, Dad, because she's dead."

"Angela!" Josie gasped.

"Dead like Christmas. Dead like Mom. Why did you think we could celebrate Christmas this year anyway?" I kicked at the tiny shards of angel arm, scattering them, then stomped on the only recognizable bits—two fingernail-sized slivers that had once been Ilona's billowing, shimmery plaster sleeve—grinding them into dust. Then I shoved away from Dad and Josie and ran to my room.

Once there, I slammed the door, leaned against it, and pressed both hands to my madly thumping heart, gulping in air. "It's okay. It doesn't matter. Who cares that she broke?" I said over and over. Then I caught sight of the photo of Mom and me that I kept on my desk and slid to the floor, curled up in a ball, and cried and cried and cried.

SIX MONTHS. SHE HAD CANCER, and it was awful, and because it's been only *six months* since Mom died, when Dad said we were having Christmas anyway, I thought he was nuts. But Josie said that maybe, somehow, keeping Mom a part of things would help us grieve.

For five seconds, it did. We played the usual hokey Christmas songs. We made our usual mint-and-marshmallow hot cocoa. We opened the Christmas trunk and got the familiar whiff of cinnamon potpourri and dust. Just like I did every year, I lifted out Mom's angel as if it were made of spun sugar. Holding Ilona high, making the usual great ceremony of it, I turned to set her on the mantel.

I think the sudden rush of tears blinded me. I think that's why Ilona's feet hit the mantel's edge, and she tilted, falling. My frantic grab for her only swatted her down, making her fall with a hundred times the force than if she'd just slipped off the mantel.

There was a light rap-a-tat-tat on my bedroom door.

"Sweets, it's me," Dad called from the hall. "Can I come in?"

"I don't care," I mumbled.

He creaked open my door, holding up Ilona. "I glued her back together. See?"

Unwillingly, I looked. Amazingly, Ilona seemed almost perfect. Almost.

"She's missing an arm." My voice sounded as brittle as Ilona had when she smashed onto the living room floor.

Dad looked at her cockeyed. "We're all missing something."

"Sure," I replied. "I'm missing Mom."

His face crumpled, and I could've kicked myself for saying that. But I didn't apologize. I kept my face turned from him, cool and tear-free.

"Angela . . ." Dad sat next to me on the floor. He used his super-gentle, world's most understanding dad voice.

I couldn't listen to whatever it was he meant to say. I scooted away and absolutely wouldn't look at him. I muttered, "It's too soon for Christmas. How could we think it wasn't?"

I heard him grunt as he stood. "Maybe it is too soon," he said, and left my room.

I sat there, alone, dry-eyed, practically dead inside, until the sun set and the room grew black. Dad and Josie had left me in peace. But I finally went downstairs.

The living room was empty. No sign of Dad or Josie anywhere, and the music and the cocoa and the Christmas trunk and the tree were all gone.

"Dad put everything back in the garage," Josie said from behind me.

"Good," I said harshly.

"Is it?" she said, as if she really wanted to know.

"Yes."

"Maybe for the decorations. But not for Christmas." And she abruptly left the room.

I followed her. She was standing by the kitchen window, her back to me, just staring out at the night, but I could tell without her speaking that she was nearly crying. Still, I asked coldly, "What does that mean?"

She swallowed hard before replying. "Oh, really, Angela. Don't you know the true meaning of Christmas?"

Her voice was sharp when it should've been understanding, so my voice went sharp too. "Definitely, yeah. Christmas isn't the gifts or the tree or the tinsel. It's Jesus being born." I plopped onto a kitchen chair. "It's still too soon."

Josie sat too, her eyes gazing into mine, almost pleading. "Even though the decorations aren't Christmas, I still want them up."

"Forgetting Mom?"

She shook her head. "Honoring her. Most of the decorations are hers." She said again, "What's the real meaning of Christmas, Angela?"

So I said, super-snarkily, "I just said, Josie. Jesus being born."

She shook her head again, impatiently this time. "Christmas points to Easter. Jesus taking away our sins. Dying for us. Giving us eternal life."

Meaning those of us who died are no longer dead. Meaning everyone who died sick is now healed and healthy. Forever and ever, perfect and whole, with Jesus.

My voice cracked. "Mom's waiting for us in heaven, isn't she?"

"Yes." Josie's voice cracked too.

I bit at my lip. "But I still can't face Christmas, or Ilona—one-armed, no longer able to enfold us with love."

"She never could, Ang. She's just plaster." Josie gently touched my hand. "But Mom will again, someday."

Mom will. And Jesus will too. Maybe the Jesus part is the best part of all.

I rubbed tears from my eyes, then abruptly stood. "I'm going to the garage."

Josie and Dad (who'd been listening from the hall) followed me. Carefully, I took Ilona from the trunk. I held her with both hands. "Let's put her on the mantel. Just Ilona, though. It's still too soon for the other stuff. But this year, and every year, Mom's favorite ornament will remind us."

"Of what, Sweets?" Dad asked quietly.

"That she's broken, like all of us. But that someday, in heaven, we'll all be made whole."

Treasure or Trash

Sandy Lipsky

THE STARKNESS OF THE KITCHEN was something I had never experienced before. A burning sensation in my nose grew as I squeezed my behemoth suitcase past the kitchen table, over the brown carpet, and down the short hallway to the "blue room." The smell of dust in the guestroom irritated my nose as I mechanically unpacked my clothes and toiletries. I swiped a finger across the glass top bedside table and looked at the thick white film. My shoulders slumped as I thought, *Mom would have dusted before I came.* I blew my nose and walked toward the kitchen. I sat at the table and waited for Dad to put his jacket away.

Big Shoes to Fill

The uneventful flight from Atlanta to Wisconsin had given me time to close my eyes and focus on breathing. Dad needed help getting ready for the holidays. I was self-employed and could easily take off the week before Christmas. To honor Mom's memory, I made a mental to-do list: prepare a meal for the nine of us, purchase gifts, wrap presents, and decorate the house. I needed brute strength and prayer to accomplish what Mom achieved with ease. Like the Energizer Bunny, her enthusiasm seemed endless. The thought of trying to fill her shoes made me want to take a nap.

"Father, help," I prayed.

Because the only bus to Janesville departed before my flight landed, I had spent the previous night in a hotel near the airport. After an early morning breakfast of homemade banana bread, I repacked my luggage. With a brisk step, I walked to the lobby to catch the hotel shuttle. Outside baggage claim at the airport, the Wisconsin Coach bus awaited to whisk me to my intended destination. Being the sole passenger on the bus caused a smile to form. No conversations were expected if I chose a seat far enough from the driver. I wasn't ready to talk.

With my head leaning back on the seat and my watery eyes looking out the window, familiar lyrics replayed silently in my mind. These were the same words I listened to repeatedly when I rode this very bus ten years ago when Dad underwent bypass surgery. Sara Groves's comforting melody soothed the beginning of an eye twitch and the heart-in-my-throat sensation. The lyrics assured that everything was going to be alright.

Superhero Traits

Dad is always right. It's annoying. In my youth, this trait caused conflict. Even so, I knew I was lucky. Words like dependable, diligent, honest, and supportive described my father. While visiting our parents years ago, my sister and I decided to take an evening walk around the block. A torrential rain took us by surprise. Blocked by fences and sideways precipitation, we struggled to find a faster way back to our folks' house.

With our clothes soaked and hair dripping, we continued to weave up and down driveways, looking for an opening. A car engine whirred behind us. We looked at each other with a knowing smile and a grateful heart. Dad to the rescue. Knowing when to show up is his superpower.

Memories of Traditions Past

Deep-rooted traditions pervaded our family Christmases. Mom assigned each member a role. Dad's job included carrying up the multiple totes from the basement. He put the eight-foot artificial tree together and placed it in the center of the large picture window located in the living room. Next, he strung red, green, and blue incandescent tubular-shaped bulbs around the branches. Once he completed the looping of the lights across the bushes in front of the house and on the metal trellis adjacent to the front door, his input neared completion. He then set up two card tables next to the plastic pine.

Collecting was one of Mom's passions—after God and family. She collected plates, dolls, coins, vases, Hummels, Swarovski's, dish sets, and Wade figurines. This list only touched the beginning of what she owned. Although not at the top of her list, ornaments held a special place in her heart. With gentle, efficient hands, Mom lifted each ornament from the original package, unwrapped it, and placed the prized possession on the card table. Once the table was full, Mom attached a small metal hook and hung them one by one on the tree. The process took hours, if not days. She owned hundreds and hundreds of them. It remains a mystery how Mom could find a place for each one. But she did.

> Dad stood on a ladder to position the star like a king placing a bejeweled crown on his adorned queen.

With the tree fully decorated, Dad stood on a ladder to position the star like a king placing a bejeweled crown on his adorned queen. Subsequently, the artist of the family placed Santa Clauses and nativity sets on shelves and cabinets. She hung stockings and wreaths on the walls. After completion, Mom plopped in her favorite chair to await the arrival of her family.

Now Mom's chair sits empty. There is a picture of her on an easel outside the entrance to the kitchen. She's wearing pink. My favorite color.

As I looked at her smile, the throb in my chest eased for a moment. I sat at the kitchen table and wrote down the mental list I had made on the plane. I took a deep breath and exhaled with a tremble.

"Father, give me strength."

Dad seemed in a fog during our decorating process. He needed questions repeated. Items he picked up disappeared, and no amount of discussion helped his recall. His step seemed slower, and the smile that frequented his face vanished from sight. Pictures of previous years from my smartphone guided the location of the holiday trimmings. With minimal guidance, Dad went through the motions he had repeated for sixty-plus years. We used the dining room to place the totes. The tree—a little crooked—stood in its usual spot. We decorated the house and cooked the food. Although our family made it through the first Christmas of loss, it felt like walking through four feet of snow in the middle of a blizzard.

> Although our family made it through the first Christmas of loss, it felt like walking through four feet of snow in the middle of a blizzard.

Traditions Repurposed

The following year, I looked forward to arriving at Dad's a week before Christmas. This would provide time for the yuletide adornments and food preparation. A new plan formed in my mind. We could repurpose our Christmas traditions.

Instead of turkey, we'd try lasagna. No more pies and cookies. I'd make bars. Dad didn't care. He was glad to see me. After we enjoyed our take-out meal from Culver's, we walked down the stairs to the basement together and carried the multiple totes to the main level. Once the seasonal embellishments were in place, I asked Dad to set up the tree.

"I took it to the dump."

"What?"

My heart raced, and my face felt hot. Words formed but got stuck in my mouth. Dad said the phrase calmly as he looked over his shoulder at me. He wanted something smaller. Could it have lights already attached? Without a word, I walked out of the living room. As I lay on the bed in the guestroom, tears flowed down the side of my face and into my ears. My stomach hurt from the verbal punch. Didn't he care about Mom? The idea to repurpose the elegant, stately pine with a spindly, pre-lit tree felt incomprehensible.

The Healing Tree

Grief is like the Mississippi River. Constantly moving, it ebbs and flows and sometimes is difficult to navigate. The tree had intertwined itself with Mom in my psyche. The ornately decorated emblem was the centerpiece of our celebration. So was Mom. The tree was cheerful, flashy, and fun. It stood sturdy, with full branches that could bear heavy loads. It greeted passing neighbors with a twinkle and a warm welcome. It was strong and beautiful. Like my mom.

> I now see there was an unspoken need to repurpose our traditions—including the tree.

I know the tree isn't the reason we celebrate Christmas. Jesus is. God so loved us and sent his precious Son as a gift to the world. Dad knew this too. I now see there was an unspoken need to repurpose our traditions—including the tree. Despite losing the love of his life, did Dad recognize the tree to be a dim shadow of what matters? A plastic, fake greenery would never replace the richness of relationship or the beauty of God's gift to the world. My father navigated the bends and turns of grief with adeptness and confidence. The ornately decorated tree was not the true centerpiece of our celebration.

It took another year for me to catch up with Dad's resolution to dump the tree Mom loved. To repurpose our Christmas tree took a beat to embrace, but it was the right one to make. The choice moved me forward. And the spindly pine's presence taught me two lessons in the process. Life moves on, and Dad was right. Again.

His Perfect Timing

Pam Whitley Taylor

VERY DECEMBER, I EAGERLY PULL my Christmas ornaments from their year-long home of bubble wrap and tissue paper. Manger scenes, candy canes, glass baubles, snowmen, and handmade ornaments abound. Some are showing the ravages of time, but they all hold precious memories for me. [6]

Among my favorites are two antique glass balls with rusty hangers and fading colors. As a little girl, I was delighted when I was old enough to hang them on our Christmas tree. The years still melt away when I see them, and my heart always transports me to a long-ago Christmas when I learned of God's faithful provision for his children.

It's been forty-eight years since that Christmas. I was twenty-six, and our only child, Ben, was two years old. That year, for the first time since Ben's birth, my husband and I planned to travel from Oklahoma to my childhood home in Mississippi to spend the holidays on the farm with my parents. I could hardly wait.

As I prepared for that trip, among the important things on my to-do list was to make a batch of peanut brittle. It was my dad's favorite candy. I'd just accomplished that feat as memories of bygone Christmases filled my heart.

I was the youngest of four children. By the time I was eight years old, I was the only child left at home. One of my fondest memories was of Daddy and me, just the two of us, bouncing around the farm in his old pickup as we searched for a Christmas tree.

Eventually, we'd find the perfect little tree. My dad would chop it down and "plant" it in a dirt-filled bucket and set it in our living room. I'd weave our big-multicolored lights through its branches, hang our glass ornaments haphazardly around it, throw whipped Ivory Soap flakes "snow" on it, and then finish up with a generous sprinkling of tinsel. As soon as I plugged in the lights, I'd call my mom and dad, and we'd all enjoy its shimmering beauty.

The ringing of the wall phone jarred me back to reality, as did the serious tone in my brother's voice.

"Pam, I hate to have to tell you this, but I have bad news. Daddy's visit to the doctor didn't go well," my brother's voice broke as he shared his news. "Daddy has been diagnosed with a brain tumor. The doctor thinks it's malignant and scheduled surgery for December 17."

I was stunned. I leaned against the kitchen counter as tears streamed down my face. My dad had recently experienced dizzy spells and numbness in one arm, but we thought it was a pinched nerve.

> I crumpled my long to-do list and flung it into the trash. What had seemed important moments before was now of no significance.

The year before, he'd retired from thirty years of teaching school. He then started many hard projects on the farm. One included cutting down several trees to mill for lumber. Since he was doing so much hard work, we hoped he'd strained a muscle. I'd not given much thought to any other possibility since he'd always been so healthy.

I crumpled my long to-do list and flung it into the trash. What had seemed important moments before was now of no significance. My sweet husband urged me to buy a plane ticket to Mississippi. He'd drive down as soon as his vacation started.

Two days later, I boarded a plane with a diaper bag slung over one shoulder and my chubby little boy on my hip. The flight seemed to take forever. As the plane descended at the Jackson Airport, I caught a glimpse of the lush green pines of Mississippi. I held Ben tightly as grief washed over me and tears streamed down my face. My shoulders ached from the stress, and so did my heart as we landed.

"Lord," I cried out in anger, "*why did this have to happen at Christmas? Please let Daddy be okay! Let Ben grow up knowing him.*"

A carousel of distressing thoughts continued to circle through my head as I debarked the plane.

To make matters worse, the Jackson hospital was too far from our home to drive back and forth. My mom, my sister, and my brothers rented motel rooms so we'd be near my dad. The extra cost strained all of our budgets.

Some Christmas, Lord.

On the second day of my dad's hospital stay, a legislator from our hometown visited. He was a family friend who had grown up on the farm next to ours. As he prepared to leave, he pulled a key from his pocket and handed it to us.

"The legislature is officially on break now, and my two roommates and I are headed home today. If you need it, our apartment is yours for the rest of December. It's not far from the hospital."

We checked out of our motel rooms and located our friend's apartment. Each of the three bedrooms had private baths, and the apartment was furnished with a washer and dryer. When my sister and I weren't at the hospital, we finished our Christmas shopping together. We all took turns staying with my dad, and we shared many sweet times together, not only at the hospital but also in our borrowed home.

On Christmas Eve, my dad was dismissed from the hospital. When we arrived home, someone had brought us a fresh-cut pine tree. My sister and I decorated it late that night. Neighbors and friends had graciously filled the house with wonderful Southern food. Although it was my dad's last Christmas as well as my last Christmas to spend on the farm, we still had a very blessed time together.

Years later, I took my grown son to the farmhouse for one last visit. My mother still owned the homestead, but she'd moved into a duplex in town. Knowing the old house would soon be torn down, I wanted Ben to see it again.

The next morning was sunshiny and cool—perfect weather for exploring the farm. The three of us eagerly drove the eight miles into the country. Once we arrived, Mother unlocked the farm door with her old skeleton key. A whiff of stale air and mildew greeted us. The house had long since been emptied of its furnishings, and leaves and roly-polies littered the floor. We were silent as we walked through. I could almost hear the laughter and see the tears experienced in the sixty years of vibrant life lived within the walls of that old house. Above all, I remembered the joy and the pain of that last Christmas there.

Then my son, Ben, and I walked outside to a storage building. Odds and ends littered the rickety old shelves. An old hard hat of my dad's, a few rusty tools, old vases, and mason jars—I'd looked through the stuff many times, but my son was much taller than I. Reaching up on a high shelf, he pulled down a dusty old box. Knowing how sentimental I was, with a big smile, he handed it to me. Lying on top were the old ornaments. I'd never seen them again after that last Christmas on the farm. Two of them remained unbroken. With tears in my eyes, I carefully picked them up as sweet memories filled my heart.

I humbly shared with Ben how angry and disappointed I'd been with God that long ago Christmas when my plans went awry. And then I shared of how I finally realized his timing was perfect. That apartment would have only been available in December, and none of us would have already had vacation time planned except for it being Christmas.

Nearly five decades have come and gone since that last Christmas on the farm, yet it is one of my most cherished memories. And each year when I unpack those two old ornaments, bittersweet memories flow once again as I am reminded that unexpected things may blindside me, but they never blindside God. His timing is perfect.

Unexpected Angel

Lisa-Anne Wooldridge

CHRISTMAS WAS COMING, AND FOR the second year in a row, my young son was struggling just to survive. We canceled all our holiday activities and plans as he fought for life and breath. His younger sister was at an age where the stress of it all was really affecting her—she wanted a happy Christmas, not endless days at the hospital. We were all at a breaking point. The weather was bleak, but the children's wing felt even bleaker. A nurse confided to me that a special kind of heaviness always settled over the ward around the holidays.

Unexpected Joy

A hospital administrator came to the room where I was struggling to entertain my daughter and comfort my son while my husband was at work. She asked if they could bring donated gifts in for the children. My daughter immediately perked up—her face was so sweet as she asked where Santa was. She insisted he must have come to the hospital, but the nurses wouldn't let him in. It was a pretty restricted floor with heavy screening of visitors, and she was just sure Santa wanted to visit. The admin laughed and told her Santa would never be sent away, but it was one of his special helpers who delivered all the presents for the children stuck in the hospital at Christmas.

147

I was grateful for any distraction and quickly agreed. A group of hospital volunteers brought in a treasure trove of gifts. I expected a small trinket or a cheap plastic toy of some kind, or maybe a stuffed animal, but this was beyond anything we could imagine. My daughter squealed as she opened the first gift. It was an Easy Bake Oven with several extra boxes of cookie and cake mix. They'd even included all the accessories! I could barely believe it—it was the number one item on her Christmas wish list. For a disorienting moment, I wondered if Santa was real after all! Next, she opened a soft doll that looked like her, with similar hair and eyes and even a nearly identical dress.

> For a disorienting moment, I wondered if Santa was real after all!

She "helped" my son open his presents too. He was fairly weak, but I could see his excitement. There were toy cars and a big track for them and some very popular wooden railway train characters and sets. I recognized it as one of the nicest sets they sold, and it included all his favorite train characters. Tears sprang up, and my throat grew tight at the sight of them. These too-expensive tank engine toys were already his obsession. He'd spend an hour or more playing with them at the toy store and was always disappointed to leave his "friends" behind.

I'd planned to buy him a simple set for Christmas, but he'd been sick most of December, and our shopping budget was whittled down to very little. Having a child in the hospital is expensive, no matter what insurance you have.

The admin stuck around to watch the kids open the presents. She was all smiles, but I caught the tears in her eyes as she watched. I asked her who had donated such wonderful, top-quality gifts to the children of strangers. She told me I'd never believe it and named a notorious biker group with a reputation for trouble. I was shocked—a little bit of fear passed through me as I considered returning the toys. The admin watched to see how I would respond. I felt a little nudge to be at peace and not be afraid.

Putting my concern aside, I said, "What a wonderful, generous surprise. If you see them again, please tell them thank you for us. They're our Christmas angels." I told her how we were struggling and how the gifts were exactly what we'd hoped to buy the kids, but everything was so hard we weren't even sure we'd have a Christmas. She was thrilled with my response and squeezed my arm.

> The gifts were exactly what we'd hoped to buy the kids.

"I'll tell them. People have no idea they do this every year. They never advertise it, but they are the first ones to donate a check when there's a fundraiser, and they do a lot of other good things people never hear about. I know it's a surprise, but they really enjoy doing something for the kids."

I pondered her words as she walked away. I was so grateful—but I was still shaken. This kind of behavior went against every ingrained perception I had about these men. I wondered if God had a hand in it because it seemed impossible otherwise.

Close Encounter of the Heavenly Kind

A few months later, in the early spring, I packed up the kids to go out for a day at the beach. My son was doing well, and we wanted to visit the tidepools, but first I needed gas for the car. I was waiting by the pump when a motorcycle roared into the spot on the other side.

The rider was dressed in leathers and sat on a big tricked-out Harley. He grabbed the nozzle and turned to fill his bike, his back to me. He was wearing a jacket with the emblem of the biker group that delivered the gifts to sick children. I gasped, and he turned his face toward me, lowering his sunglasses slightly to look at me.

I could see he was tense, ready to react to any sort of threat or perhaps intimidate someone with his glare, but I was beaming at him. He seemed surprised—probably wondering why this soccer mom with a minivan was grinning at him like an idiot. I came around to his side of the pump as he shifted to stand between me and his bike.

"I never thought I'd get the chance," I said. I stuck out my hand to shake his, but he just stared at it as if it was something suspicious. I moved in a little closer, defying every shaking nerve in my body to stand nearly toe to toe with him. He was a big man, at least six-foot-three and around three hundred pounds, heavily muscled. One corner of his mouth lifted with a hint of amusement, but he remained silent.

I just looked up into his eyes and said, "Thank you. I just wanted to say thank you." Tears welled up in my eyes as I recalled the wonderful Christmas we'd had thanks to those generous toys. My voice grew a little husky and tight as I continued, "You saved Christmas." I was sure I wasn't making sense, but I was doing my best.

He cocked his head at me, clearly not knowing what to think. I could see his shoulders relaxing. "Do I know you?"

> "I don't know how you guys knew. It's like they had Christmas angels looking out for them."

I shook my head no. I sucked in a breath and said, "My son was in the hospital—it was touch and go—right before Christmas. And they brought us toys from you guys. My son and my daughter were both so happy. We couldn't afford any of that. My kids were scared and sad, and you guys brought Christmas to them. You have no idea how much it meant to us. It's like God sent you. The train set and the little oven they got, those were the things we wanted to get them, I don't know how you guys knew. It's like they had Christmas angels looking out for them."

A Confession

As I was speaking, his eyes grew wide, and his eyebrows raised nearly to his hairline.

"That was me," he said, finally speaking. "I bought the oven, and my buddy picked out the trains. A bunch of us brought gifts and dropped them off." He looked over at my van. "Are your kids—" He blinked rapidly several times and cleared his throat. "Are your kids okay now?" He looked a little bit afraid of the answer, so I called through my open window to the children.

"Come on out, guys. I want you to meet an angel."

I went to the van and opened the back door to let my children out and walked them over to the man. I said, "This is the person who brought you those toys at the hospital. My daughter hugged my leg and waved up at him shyly. My son walked straight over and hugged the man around the legs. The big, scary biker had tears rolling down his face. He picked up my son and held him up like any dad might do.

He said, "I'm so glad you're doing better. You stay well, now. Okay?"

My son nodded, very seriously, and said, "You're a good angel."

He put my son down, and I helped the kids back into their booster seats and closed the door.

I felt something stirring in my heart. God had used this unlikely "angel" to minister to us, but we were meant to meet him and give him a gift in return. The story of the prodigal son briefly came to mind, and I felt sure that this man was being called to come home.

A Parting Gift

When I turned back toward him, the man seemed a little stiff and uncomfortable, and he'd wiped away any trace of tears. I placed my hand on his arm and said, "God sees the heart. And so do we. You know who your real Father is." I squeezed his forearm and said, "You have a lot of love in your heart, and I think that's who you really are."

I could see the dam about to break as he tried to keep his emotions locked down. He nodded, and I knew it was time for me to go. I walked over and put the gas cap back on, double checked seatbelts, and drove away. I smiled as a thought crossed my mind. Never judge a book by its cover. Or its leather jacket.

The Good and Perfect Gift

Betty Predmore

CHANGE CAN BE DIFFICULT, ESPECIALLY when it involves precious holiday traditions that have been a part of your heart for as long as you can remember. While we might resist the change, hanging on to the past with every ounce of strength, we often see that the new thing isn't so bad.

For all my adult life, through raising four kids and adopting three more, I have clung tightly to the Christmas traditions of my past. I have based the success of my holidays on how closely they resembled my Christmases of long ago.

I have also added my own touches to those traditions to make them even more meaningful. Every year, my daughters gather at my house after Thanksgiving to help me decorate for the Christmas season. Each year, we bundle the family up in as many cars as it takes and drive around looking at Christmas lights. On Christmas Eve, new pajamas are received. And Christmas Eve has become our game night, with the whole family playing awesome and ridiculous games that I have created throughout the years.

Laughter abounds, and the competition is fierce. There are high-pitched squeals of delight from the winners and moans of angst from the losers, and it is an all-around great time. We stuff ourselves with more desserts than necessary and share in this rowdy and robust family time.

Always at the root of these Christmas celebrations are the memories of those Christmases long ago, and trying my best to recreate that feeling.

An Old Gift

The Christmas celebrations buried deep in my heart are the ones where my sweet Granny's house was the center of the celebration. Christmas Eve included her beloved children and grandchildren joyfully crowded into her living room. While this was a rather small room, to a child who adored everything about this larger-than-life woman, it was the grandest place to gather for occasions, big or small.

Christmas Eve was about gathering for a delicious meal, followed by scrumptious pies and cakes that were lovingly prepared with an extra spoonful of love added to each recipe. Conversations were loud, and the excitement of a gaggle of little cousins was even louder. Christmas Day, we all gathered there again, enjoying another traditional meal together and spending the afternoon enjoying the time of togetherness.

> The gifts aren't what stood out to me in that moment or in my memory, even to this day.

I have a specific memory of one of those Christmas Eve gatherings. I was probably six or seven years old at the time. Like all the cousins, I had claimed my spot on the floor and waited with eager anticipation as my pile of presents was placed beside me. I don't remember what the gifts were that year. The gifts aren't what stood out to me in that moment or in my memory, even to this day.

What struck me in that moment, and what is so clear in my mind over fifty years later, is the sense of security I felt. Sitting on that floor, surrounded by my family, amid the adults talking, the kids squealing with excitement, and the sea of wrapping paper that covered the carpet was the sense of absolute security. I was in the best of places with the greatest of people, and I knew it.

That is what family traditions offer us. They give us a sense of familiarity, a sense of family, the feeling of continuity, and the opportunity to replicate our past, bringing it into our present. Often our present is startlingly different from our past, and those traditions are the only things that can offer us an anchor to those pieces of our past we long for.

A Treasured Gift

As a mama with kids of my own, keeping up those traditions was important to me. Gathering with family on Christmas Eve, preparing all my Granny's specialties, and doing my best to provide that sense of joy, excitement, and security to my kids was always at the forefront of my stress-induced mind. In my mind, if I didn't do it *just like that*, I wouldn't be doing it right.

For many years, this was my mindset. Perfection equaled imitation. Looking back, I can see that I went overboard in my efforts. Retrospect is often an enlightening tool. When we are living in the moment, we often don't recognize the reasoning behind our actions. Time has a way of opening our eyes to the reality of a situation.

The reality of my situation, which I discovered after many, many years, was that I was chasing after the memories of my childhood. I was setting myself up for disappointment year after year because I wouldn't let myself believe that those days were now just a memory and life would never be exactly like that again.

Being caught up in the past can keep us from enjoying the present and being excited about the future. Trying to achieve what is unachievable will keep us feeling frustrated and discouraged. That is not what Christmas is about. Christmas symbolizes joy, peace, hope, promise, and love.

I have come to realize that Christmas doesn't need to imitate the holidays of my past. Perfection is not required, nor is it needed. Christmas is the most special when it imitates the love of Christ, even if that looks different to my family every year.

A New Gift

Our family is growing. There are in-laws, grandbabies, and new friends. As our family grows and changes, so will the ways in which we celebrate. My adult children are looking to add their own traditions to their families. As much as I don't relish the change, I know it's necessary. Gone are my expectations of imitating the past.

I am learning to *go with the flow*, as they say, and take one Christmas at a time. I am discovering that there are other ways to measure the beauty of Christmas besides the similarity of the Christmases of my long-ago days.

> What truly counts on this special day each year, and during all the holidays we celebrate, is that there is love.

What truly counts on this special day each year, and during all the holidays we celebrate, is that there is love. The important thing is that we honor the glorious reason for the season instead of getting caught up in exactly how things should go.

Is there grace? Is there joy? Are minor offenses being forgiven in the spirit of the season? Are generosity and compassion for others overflowing?

Those are the vital traditions to pass on. What we eat, when we open gifts, or what games we play have no importance when compared to celebrating the birth of the Savior. The extent of how generous we are with those in need is far more important than what we receive.

The Sweetest Gift

Do I want my grandchildren to have beautiful memories of their Christmases with Grammy? Absolutely! Is it my prayer that they always feel secure and content in our celebrations? You bet! The greatest gift I can give them is not the presents under the tree or the traditions passed from generation to generation. My sweetest offering to them is keeping my focus on the birth of our Savior and sharing that love with them. Making sure Jesus is in their hearts is the most important thing during Christmas and every day. "Whatever is good and perfect is a gift coming down to us from God our Father, who created all the lights in the heavens" (James 1:17). He is the perfect gift, yesterday, today, and tomorrow.

Life and the pursuit of perfection have taught me that I don't have to imitate to celebrate. The traditions of the past take up a huge space in my heart, but there is still room for new memories and new ways of making Christmas special. If I keep my focus on Jesus and live out that example, Christmas will be beautiful, precious, and filled with joy. I am not perfect, but he is.

I will still be in the best of places, with the greatest of people, and I know it. And that sounds perfect to me.

After Christmas Pity Party

Barbara Syvertson

AFTER A LONG STEAMY SHOWER to loosen my cough, I dragged my feverish body under the covers of our bed. Alone. My husband, Ed, who is usually very helpful and attentive was neither that night.

"I'll sleep in the guest room," he offered. He didn't want to catch what I had, and he also had his own issues with a stomach bug he picked up at our dismal motel the night before. It was only December 26, and already our post-Christmas plans had been ruined.

My cough and my self-pity kept me awake most of the night. I'd never felt so sick. *What if I fall asleep and never wake up? What if I am gasping for air and Ed doesn't hear me? Why didn't I go to the emergency room on our drive back home?*

When I reached for another box of tissues, I spotted my mother's old and worn Bible sitting on the bedside table. I didn't need another reason to cry, but there it was. Mom had died a few years before, and this Bible was another precious connection to her that I was happy to receive from my sister the day before as a Christmas gift.

I thought that maybe looking through her underlined and tattered Bible might bring me a timely word from the Lord. It didn't happen. Just the opposite. It created the perfect conditions for a pity party. A virtual storm of physical pain, emotional pain, and spiritual pain that escalated to hurricane proportions. You know pity parties. They are not fun like the word *party* implies. What followed was an emotional free fall.

NyQuil and Tissues

"I miss you, Mom, so much."

"If you were alive, I could call you even though it's 2:00 a.m. You would answer as if I hadn't even woken you. And your sympathy would be just what I wanted. Your motherly advice urging me to keep it all in perspective would be just what I needed."

"I have no one tonight."

"No one cares about how sick I am."

"I am sick, tired, and unlovable. No one loves me."

"No one will ever care about me."

"Someday, I'll be dying all alone, and no one will come to visit me."

Self-pity creates a nosedive. I just completely dove into the deep end of the pity pool, and now I couldn't even tread water.

> I just completely dove into the deep end of the pity pool, and now I couldn't even tread water.

I cried hard. The kind of crying that is painful when you have a deep, barking cough. It was now the gagging, cough-cry that takes all your energy and uses all your tissues. And it went on and on. Poor me. Woe to me. Although my circumstances weren't as severe as the self-pity that accompanied them, I still gave in to it. I finally had the good sense to take some NyQuil and fall asleep. Sometimes a good night's rest is what your body is actually craving.

After a decent night of sleep, a hot shower, and a cup of coffee, I headed out to the doctor's office that had graciously squeezed me into their busy schedule. I left with a slight spring in my step, knowing that I would get help and thankful that I hadn't died during the night. Yes, very dramatic, I know.

Stethoscopes and Tongue Depressors

As anticipated, the doctor was kind and compassionate but took an unusually long time listening to my heart and lungs.

"You were wise to call off your trip and come home. You have a severe case of bronchitis and a touch of pneumonia. In addition to these prescriptions, you need lots of rest, fluids, and Tylenol. That is a bad cough you have there."

I felt such relief. My body was still sick, but I didn't need the hospital travel bag that was lying in the back of the van. My cough made it hard to talk, so I texted my husband from the parking lot to tell him about the appointment and the diagnosis. While still in the van, I got a text from my friend Traci. She asked if she could stop by the house. I told her I was sick and needed to stop for a prescription, but then I'd be home. She said she wouldn't come in—she just wanted to drop something off.

Frozen Lasagna and a Flaming Potato

Shortly after I got home, Traci showed up with a beautiful picnic-style wicker basket for me. Through coughs and an opened storm door, I told her about our canceled trip. I told her about our seven-month-old grandson having RSV and how miserable he felt during our Christmas Eve family gathering. I told her about the family member who put a raw potato in the microwave and set the timer for far too long, causing the potato to catch on fire. Literal flames were visible inside the microwave as the smoke alarms blared and smoke filled the house. We ran around opening doors and windows and setting up fans in the middle of a cold December.

This happened while our grandson was getting a steam-breathing treatment upstairs. The scene was so absurd that my sister and I were just laughing. I laughed and coughed my way into a fresh pair of jeans. The lasagna we had planned for dinner was still frozen after the prescribed time in the oven. Take-out bags filled with burgers and fries from a nearby Wendy's was our unexpected Christmas Eve dinner before heading to our church service.

Our son and two-year-old grandson left, as planned, to drive for nine hours through the night to his in-laws in Indiana. Our daughter-in-law and their sick baby were flying to Indiana the next morning. We needed to take them to the airport.

"So, you obviously didn't go to Florida as planned?" was Traci's reasonable question.

"Well, after the airport, we drove eight hours south, spent the night in a cheesy motel in North Carolina and drove back the next morning. I knew I needed to get to a doctor."

Warm Chicken Soup and Pumpkin Roll

I thanked Traci profusely for her kindness and generosity in bringing us a basket of food. After I closed the door, I opened the basket to find two mason jars filled with still-warm, homemade chicken soup, a plate of fresh mini grilled cheese sandwiches, a homemade pumpkin roll, cheerful bouquet of flowers, and a precious note of encouragement to me.

Something at the bottom of the basket caught my attention. It hit me hard. It went deeper than the emotion of receiving the beautiful basket. I wept. Have you ever experienced the kind of tears that spring from a heart full of amazement at the personal nature of God's love?

> Something at the bottom of the basket caught my attention. It hit me hard. . . . I wept.

You see, in the excitement of getting a better diagnosis than I expected, and having drugs to fix me up, I had completely forgotten about my bedroom pity party the night before. I forgot that I had basically fallen asleep thinking I was going to die alone and unloved. There in the bottom of the basket was a small wooden plaque with three simple words painted on it: You are loved.

When I read it, it could easily have spoken to my heart like this, "Oh Traci loves me. She's here for me." It would be true for sure. But it immediately struck a deeper chord in me. *God loves me and cares about me and will always take care of me. Today. Tomorrow. In my home. In a nursing home. With no one around. With crowds around. I am loved by him.* The complete opposite of a pity party. That was the clear and powerful message I heard when I read that small phrase.

I hadn't prayed the previous night. I just wallowed.

I hadn't told anyone about my hours of despair the previous night. Not Ed nor Traci.

But God knew.

Whispers and Wooden Signs

I finally called Traci to tell her how impactful that gift was to me. I confided in her about my visceral reaction to my mom's Bible, my nighttime pity party, and my overwhelming feeling of being so unloved. It was embarrassing to admit. I knew it wasn't true. But downward spirals and depressing conclusions are the chip and dip of this kind of party.

Traci said with tenderness in her voice, " When I woke up this morning, I knew God wanted me to do this. It was as if God whispered to me, 'Okay, Traci, today I need you to show Barb that I love her and will always take care of her.'"

Traci followed the still voice of God, not knowing anything about my vulnerable situation. The soup is long gone, but that little wooden sign still sits on my nightstand to remind me of how loving and caring God is. It is a reminder that I serve and worship a God who sends baskets full of what I need when I need it. He hears my overly dramatic cries and offers grace not shame.

The Christmas Card

Heather Norman Smith

"ARE YOU SURE YOU DON'T want to join the others?" The young nurse placed a gentle hand on Stephen's shoulder. "We're going to drink hot chocolate and sing carols by the tree."

Stephen crossed his arms and rested tight fists on the armrests of his wheelchair. "No, thanks. I'm not really a fan of hot chocolate, and I don't sing. I'll be fine here."

The woman, clad in blue scrubs, shrugged and left Stephen's room at the end of North Hall, closing the door behind her.

After two months of living at the rehab facility, Molly, the head nurse on his hall, was Stephen's favorite of the ones who cared for him. But the idea of *needing* to be cared for hadn't gotten any easier. Most of the other patients were over eighty years old, people learning to walk again after a stroke or long-term illness. Car accident victims in their thirties, like Stephen, were in the minority at Fairmont Rehabilitation Center. But Stephen wasn't really a *victim*. He'd put himself in that wheelchair.

He wheeled to the window and watched snow falling in the glow of the streetlight, second-guessing his decision not to go to the Christmas Eve party. Just because he was stuck in rehab for at least another month didn't mean he should abandon all celebration. Maybe if any of his friends or business associates had come to visit him for the holidays, he'd be in the Christmas spirit, but he hadn't had a visitor in weeks. He didn't blame them. Why would anyone come to see him when all he'd cared about before the accident was his climb to the top of the corporate ladder?

The faintest sound of a piano soon came from the common area at the end of the hall where each of the four corridors of the facility converged. Then came singing. Maybe "Jingle Bells?" Stephen wheeled to the door and listened for a moment. He'd liked that one as a kid. He opened the door and wheeled himself into the hallway. When the song was over, the voices joined in "We Wish You a Merry Christmas."

"Not much to be merry about this year," Stephen muttered. "Not so much as a Christmas card in the mail."

The row of doors on each side of the hall added insult to injury. Some were covered with Christmas cards, but each of them had at least one. Every door except—

Stephen turned his head. His door *did* have a card, secured by a single piece of transparent tape. But who had put it there? It hadn't been there when he'd gone to physical therapy earlier. The facility must have given them to every patient.

The front of the red card had an outline of a church and a shiny Christmas star in gold foil. Stephen wheeled closer, reached up, and opened the card, careful not to pull the tape loose. In a pretty script, beneath the printed "Merry Christmas" message, it read: "From someone who understands." The card was signed "E.J."

How strange. Who was E.J.? One of the nurses, maybe? He hadn't made friends with any of the residents. And what did this person understand about him?

Stephen grasped the wheels of his chair and pushed until he reached the next room on North Hall. Each door had a sign beside it with the patient's name. A Mr. Jones occupied the room next to Stephen's, but his first name was Robert. The occupant of the room across the hall was named Cynthia. No E.J. there. Curiosity nudged Stephen down the long, empty hallway fairly gleaming with its white walls and white tile under fluorescent lights. He checked each sign. None of the patients had a first name starting with E.

As he neared the common area, the scent of pine grew more intense, and the singing became louder. Stephen stilled the chair and listened. "Silent night, holy night, all is calm, all is bright." The song held a tender reverence, and the old people sounded clear and strong as they sang. In his youth, Stephen had believed in the miracle of Christmas, but his faith had withered over time, like the neglected plants in his apartment had probably done.

Someone stepped around the corner and stopped just short of bumping into his chair. *Molly.*

"Hey there. I was coming back to see if you'd change your mind. You're the only patient on my hall that's not at the party."

Stephen cleared his throat. "No, I, uh, I haven't changed my mind. Hey, do you know who taped a Christmas card to my door?"

One corner of Molly's mouth turned upward. "I did. But it's not from me. I just delivered it."

"So, who's it from?"

"I can't say for sure, but it's from another resident. Their nurse put it in my mailbox to bring to you. She works on West Hall. If you're on a search, you might start there."

"West Hall. Got it."

Molly gave him a tentative stare. "Merry Christmas, Stephen. I hope you find what you need."

An odd warmth washed over him at her words. She wasn't talking about the mystery sender. Molly turned and headed back toward the Christmas Eve party. Stephen followed her into the common room, keeping close to the wall and away from the festivities, then he made a right and started down West Hall, checking the signs beside each door as he went.

Three doors down, on the left, Stephen's heart skipped a beat at the sight of a familiar name. *Emma Jennings.* A patient had the same name as the woman who'd been driving the car he slammed into on the highway because he was texting a client instead of paying attention to the road. He'd read the name in the police report and the insurance paperwork, but he hadn't met her. It *couldn't* be the same person.

Stephen held his breath as he knocked on the door.

A woman, probably a couple of years younger than he was, with long, amber-colored hair, answered. Kind eyes shined at him from her seated position in a wheelchair like his. Even with a deep, dark scar on her right cheek, the woman was beautiful.

"Hi, Stephen." She cast a timid look downward. "You got the Christmas card?"

"I—I um, yes. Thank you. Are *you* . . ."

She wheeled her chair backward, an invitation for him to enter. Stephen crossed the threshold as a new song rang out from down the hallway.

"I'm Emma. Yes, *that* Emma."

Confusion swirled in Stephen's mind like the snowflakes outside the window.

"How long have you been here? And how did you know about me?"

"About a month. It's taken me that long to work up the courage to reach out to you."

A month. She'd had to stay in the hospital longer than he had. Her compact car had been no match for his SUV. An awkward silence passed between them as he waited for the answer to his second question.

"Our nurses talk to one another. When I first came, they figured out that you and I were injured in the same accident, and my nurse, Becca, told me you were here."

Had Molly really *not* known that the card was from Emma? Either way, she'd led him here.

"I wanted to meet you," Emma said, "but I was afraid you wouldn't want to talk to me. I thought the card would be a good first step, so to speak." She blushed as she looked down at her motionless legs.

"Afraid I wouldn't want to talk to you? I don't understand. Why do you even want to talk to me?"

He hadn't confessed to texting and driving. He'd lied and said he swerved to miss a dog. Still, Emma knew the accident wasn't *her* fault.

"We've been through a similar experience," she said. "I think I can relate to some of what you're dealing with. And vice versa."

"But if it wasn't for me, you wouldn't be in this place, in that chair."

Emma twirled a strand of hair around her finger, then bit her lip. "That's one way of looking at it. But I choose to focus on being grateful. I'm thankful to still be alive. Life is a gift, and I can't waste mine living in self-pity."

A gift. What a remarkable thought. As if someone pulled back the shades of Stephen's mind, Emma's words shined into the dark corners and brought with them a sudden hope. Life *was* a gift. Even without visitors and Christmas presents, his very existence was indeed a gift.

An invisible weight lifted from Stephen's shoulders. "I think it's a gift that I've met you," he said. The happy tone of his voice sounded foreign.

A rosy hue washed over Emma's cheeks once again, and Stephen shifted in his chair. Maybe he'd been too bold. But his wonder at her perspective and his relief that she didn't hate him overshadowed embarrassment. How was she able to see the accident in such a different way than he had?

Stephen's focus landed on the gold cross pendant on Emma's necklace, shiny against her fair skin. Maybe that's what made the difference—*faith*. The thought stirred joy Stephen had long forgotten.

"I, uh . . . I guess I should thank our nurses for connecting us." He let out a nervous chuckle. "If I could, I'd run out and buy a Christmas present for both of them."

"Not getting me fired for violating privacy rules will be good enough for me."

Stephen turned at the sound of Molly's voice. She stood in the doorway beside another nurse, presumably Becca. Both women wore giant smiles.

"You don't have to worry about that," Stephen said, smiling back.

"Well, then it really is a merry Christmas." Molly gave her co-worker a playful nudge.

"I agree." Stephen nodded at the nurses then turned back to his new friend. "Thank you again for the card, Emma. Maybe you'd like to join me at the party?"

She beamed, an angelic glow on her face. "That sounds like a great idea."

Stephen looked forward to getting to know Emma Jennings. What better way to start than with a cup of hot chocolate and Christmas carols by the tree?

Jars of Clay

Gayle Veitenheimer

"So the Word became human and made his home among us. He was full of unfailing love and faithfulness. And we have seen his glory, the glory of the Father's one and only Son." (John 1:14)

Clay. He who formed Adam now coated himself. A dusty mask all his own, hiding the glory within.

Clay. Baby-sized. Baby-shaped. The Word made flesh. Muddy little fingerprints, uniquely his.

Clay. Makes me wonder about the flesh that enveloped his glory. Did his hair stand on end in awe of the one whose head it covered? Did organs, blood vessels, and lungs thrill in their service to the Great Physician?

Clay. Soft and pliable in the hands of the Master Potter.

But clay hardens in the sunlight. As the Son grew, the clay cracked, and glory flashed the earth.

Clay, mixed with spit in the palm of his hand and applied to the eyes of a man born blind—who, after washing, was blind no more.

Clay. A pitcher pouring Living Water.

Clay. A platter serving the Bread of Life.

Clay. A lamp offering the Light of the World.

Until one day, the clay was broken.

Its contents spilled.

Its treasure revealed.

A gift for all who would receive.

What a miracle.

But perhaps an even greater miracle is this. The jar of clay, the Son of God and Son of Man, joined the Master Potter, and more jars were fashioned.

> "For God knew his people in advance, and he chose them to become like his Son, so that his Son would be the firstborn among many brothers and sisters. And having chosen them, he called them to come to him. And having called them, he gave them right standing with himself. And having given them right standing, he gave them his glory." (Romans 8:29–30)

Clay. Multiplied.

Miracle Child.

The firstborn of many.

All miracles.

For we, too, are pitchers pouring Living Water.

We, too, are platters serving the Bread of Life.

We, too, are lamps offering the Light of the World.

Jars of clay, temples of the Holy Spirit.

> "We now have this light shining in our hearts, but we ourselves are like fragile clay jars containing this great treasure. This makes it clear that our great power is from God, not from ourselves." (2 Corinthians 4:7)

What a miracle.

Is There Room for Me?

Mary Anne Quinn

SEEKING A PLACE OF REFUGE amid the hustle and bustle of the Christmas season, I shuffle a path through paper, ribbon, tags, and gifts to curl up in my comfy-cozy chair with a mug of peppermint tea. White lights winding through the branches of our tree twinkle like stars in the dark sky of our living room, illuminating a miniature Victorian village surrounding an electric ice rink. I flip a switch and smile as a tiny family, bundled up in long wool coats, hats, and scarves, glides and twirls to tinny tunes offering "tidings of comfort and joy." The Christmas card worthy scene calms my frayed nerves but fails to bring the comfort my heart longs for.

A sparkly beaded ornament I crafted as a little girl at a church Christmas bazaar catches my attention and reminds me this longing originated long before my latest shopping run or gift-wrapping frenzy. I feel very present to eight-year-old me, who was loved but not always understood emotionally or spiritually. Every year, I would hold my battery-operated candle in the sheet-robed, tinsel-haloed angel choir in the Sunday school pageant and put my whole heart into singing:

Be near me, Lord Jesus
I ask thee to stay

Close by me forever
And love me I pray [7]

I so wanted those words to be real. More real than the glitter and sequins I used to fashion my ornament. I wanted them to be personal. More personal than tags with my name on gifts under the tree. Did Jesus even know my name? Did he really "look down from the sky" and see *me*? Know *me*? Love *me*?

And I didn't want to wait until Jesus took "all the dear children in [his] tender care" up to heaven to "live with him there"[8] before I could talk to him and hear him answer back—to experience him in some tangible way, even if I couldn't actually touch him. I never shared my longing with anyone because no one had ever told me that what I was longing for was even possible. I just wanted it to be possible because I wanted it so badly.

I was twenty-two when the light of Jesus's personal love for me broke through the darkness of my life and into the God void in my heart, and Jesus spoke his invitation, "I want you to belong to me forever." The first Christmas I knew the one whose birthday we were celebrating— who was not only near me but present in my heart—remains the most meaningful and special to me. I have celebrated many Christmases since then with dozens of cookies, carols, and classic black-and-white movies. Handel's Messiah sing-along concerts with the Lyric Opera of Chicago were the closest I've ever come to singing with a real angel choir. I have even celebrated a palm-tree-lit Christmas on a beach in the Caribbean.

> I wonder if the more Christmas I have in my life, the less room I have for Jesus in my heart.

But tonight, sorrow over a challenging year of loss and isolation overshadows my joy. I wonder if the more Christmas I have in my life, the less room I have for Jesus in my heart. And maybe the less room for me in Christmas? Less room in all the merriment for the places in my heart that aren't feeling merry and bright. The places where I feel alone, longing to feel known, understood, welcome. Longing for a gift that doesn't come under a tree.

Room for Jesus

I look across the room at our nativity set. Handed down from my husband John's grandmother to his mother to us, it has been the centerpiece of his family's Christmas décor—and celebration of the birth of Jesus—for almost a hundred years. The wooden stable is primitive and rough-hewn. The paint on the original plaster figurines is crackled and worn bare in places, the plastic on the two replacement sheep over-shiny, the inhabitants of the stable tippy on the uneven floor.

> We focus so much this time of year on making room for Jesus

More beloved than fancy, it still conveys the regal as well as the primitive aspects of the original Christmas setting. It's always been the first decoration to be set out each year, and my husband has had the honor of arranging the figurines since he was a teenager. The positions of Mary and Joseph in their caring, adoring postures, along with the scruffy shepherds, regal wise men, and humble animals, may shift somewhat from year to year, but their focus is always centered on the baby Jesus. And John always makes sure there is sufficient space within this holy menagerie for anyone in any part of the room to have a clear view of the Christ child as well.

We focus so much this time of year on making room for Jesus—in our busyness, our celebrations, our lives. A holly-ringed magnet occupying center stage of my refrigerator door proclaims, "There is room in my heart for Jesus." You may have the same or similar sayings accessorizing your holiday décor, but have you ever secretly wondered, as I do, *Is there room in Christmas, in that stable, for me? Does Jesus have room in his heart for my heart even when my heart is more Scrooge-like than angelic? For my joy and sorrow and every emotion in between?*

As I breathe in the steamy aroma of liquid candy cane, I settle back into the squishy cushions to better take in the view of the brightly colored collage of decorations on our tree. This time, my gaze is drawn to the path of glitter-gilded names of Jesus ornaments that grace what we call our "worship tree." King of Kings. Lord of Lords. Prince of Peace. My heart whispers a prayer: "Jesus, my heart needs a place of peace."

Room for a Child's Heart

A picture forms in my mind's eye of myself as a very young child standing before the first living nativity. The tenderness in Mary's eyes beckons me to enter in. I toddle over to the manger, grasp the side to steady myself, and peer over the edge into the face of Jesus. The wood is rough, the hay scratchy, the strips of cloth scant. But Jesus lies there, peaceful and content.

The shimmering light of the real Christmas star dances softly on his cheeks. One tiny tear glistens under a fringe of eyelashes, reassuring me that unlike the idealized baby I sang about as a child, "no crying he makes,"[9] this Jesus is real and approachable.

A thought tiptoes in. If God chose Mary and Joseph and this manger in this stable to care for and shelter his Son, this must be a safe and good place to be. If God made room here for Jesus, might Jesus make room here for me?

I pull my toddler self up into the manger and snuggle in close to Jesus. He feels soft and sweet. Mary helps me settle and brushes a strand of hair from my face. Joseph shifts his position to better shield us from the brisk night air. The cow and the donkey make snuffly noises to say, "You are welcome here, too, little one."

The thundering voices of angels praising God and declaring his favor upon the shepherds and all God's children soften as they float across hills and valley. Their glorious song transforms into a soothing lullaby to the one who traveled across the greatest divide to make his dwelling with us. The soft tones brush over us like butterfly kisses, with the reassurance that embraced in our father's heart, we are never far from home. Our place of peace.

Room for Our Whole Hearts

I rest here awhile, soaking in the presence of my down-to-earth Prince of Peace. Then, with empty mug and settled heart, I feel ready to again take up my preparations to ring the bells of Christmas cheer and celebrate Jesus's humble yet eternity-changing birthday. Determined not to lose the quiet yet certain truth: Jesus didn't come for the party; he came for the lonely.

> Jesus didn't come for the party; he came for the lonely.

Does "no room at the inn" ever sound like the story of your life? Do you ever wonder, as I have, *Does Jesus have room for me?* Whether our pain evokes ghosts of Christmas past, present, or future, it matters to Jesus. Wherever in our lives—in our hearts—we feel the least merry, that is the very place Jesus would most like to be right now.

Immanuel. With me. With you.

Cradlesong

Maureen Miller

MY NAME IS MARY.

Not yet fifteen, I've given birth to my firstborn son. There will be others, no doubt, but there can never, never again, be a firstborn.

Joseph is my good husband. He works with wood much like my mama taught me to work with dough, shaping it into something life-giving and life-sustaining. So, too, this man—shaping wood, giving it form, like this cradle.

> *Sweet Mother Mary—*
> *Labored Life for all the world,*
> *Rose daughter to Son.*

Each night, as I swaddle our baby before placing him down in the bed made by Joseph's tender though calloused hands, I remember again Jesus's first bed.

Merely a manger, hard and cold under a starlit sky, it was made to offer sustenance to sheep—grain fed to them by the shepherds abiding in the fields just outside Bethlehem. Particularly, these men and boys kept watch on the hillside near the Tower of the Flock, where the sacrificial lambs were born.

Just as I've done on so many occasions, these shepherds, too, would swaddle their newborns, then lay them in mangers with hopes of keeping them free from bumps and bruises. After all, it doesn't take the wisdom of a shepherd to know how playful day-old lambs can be, skipping and frolicking almost from birth.

But not these lambs, not those born on the Midgal Eder hillside. They're never permitted to play like the others. Rather, from the start, they're each kept confined so they might be perfect for sacrifice.

Thus, it's no wonder the shepherds knew right where to find us after the angels appeared to them in the night sky on the outskirts of that tiny town. The celestial being proclaimed, "The Savior—yes, the Messiah, the Lord—has been born today in Bethlehem, the city of David! And you will recognize him by this sign: You will find a baby wrapped snugly in strips of cloth, lying in a manger."[10]

I'll never forget—not as long as I live—how that throng of dirty men and boys, along with more sheep than I could count, approached the stable that starry night. Tentative at first, they came, one by one, to see for themselves the baby we'd placed in the stable's feeding trough.

I was tired. Had just closed my eyes, having nursed our son. From where I lay resting in the straw, I could hear Jesus—those melodic noises he made with his little lips, smacking them so. Joseph, bending low beside me, brushing a wisp of stray hair from my brow, chuckled. "He's content, Mary. Sleepy and content."

Hearing a rustle at the cave's entrance, Joseph rose with a start. Instinctively, my husband lifted a protective hand. "Who's there?"

When no one answered, he removed the lantern from its hook and then, holding it up, took several steps. "Who's . . . who's there?" Joseph called again.

It was then we heard a quiet voice. "The . . . the angel . . . he told us to—"

Stepping into light, the shepherds' leader squinted, trying to see for himself what the angel had promised. "We were told . . . we'd find—"

"A baby? Yes, our deliverer?" Having found my voice, I continued. "Come. Come see for yourselves."

And then, one by one, they came—to witness what they'd been told that they, in turn, might go and tell, which they did, their message shared throughout Bethlehem.

Oh, I'll never forget. After all, these unlikely, lowly visitors were our first—the first, in fact, to welcome our newborn baby to the world. And somehow, somehow, it just made sense.

But I won't deny that being home is best. Having our son in this familiar space—the events of the not-so-distant past seem, well, they seem almost like a dream.

Sometimes, as I rock Jesus, watching his eyes fight sleep—not wanting to miss a moment of the day—I sing to him of those shepherds.

O Little One, my little Lamb—
Let not your heart be worried,
For angels announced your timely birth,
And thus, the shepherds hurried.

They knew just where to find the babe
Wrapped in clothes of white,
For it was there that they, too, had
Swaddled lambs so tight.

There's more to the song, this lullaby I often sing to my boy, but honestly, I rarely can get through the words, so choked on tears I become.

That salty sting—it pierces my heart, truth be told, and it's then I want to somehow forget the bitter truth. Only hold to the sweetness of his breath, breathe him in but never exhale for fear that, in doing so, I'll have to share him with the world.

And it's in such moments by his cradle when I feel I should never have been called the favored one—blessed among women. Because, another truth be told, I'm merely a selfish girl. Nothing more.

So often my knuckles grow white from gripping the edge of his bed, this cradle carved by a good and decent man who listened to God when everything in him likely wanted to flee from the call to take me as his wife. But he's a burden-bearer, my sweet Joseph.

Once, not long ago, he walked up from behind as I sat singing to our son. He must have known, sensed somehow, that his strong and weathered hands were needed for the task of removing the vice grip I'd placed on the cradle's edge. He approached me silently, perhaps listening for a moment to the lullaby I sang until he heard my voice break.

It was then he knelt down and placed his hands over mine, my fingers relaxing simply at his touch. He has a way, my Joseph, and his gentleness has often softened my heart, which, quite honestly, threatens to harden so that no sword can pierce it.

After all, we both know, Joseph and me, what sharing our son with the world will mean. And even as I treasure God's many good and precious promises up in my soul, there's always that lurking shadow trying to steal my peace and joy.

But just as I feel I'll be overcome with sorrow, Jesus laughs, and suddenly, the room is filled with light, and love spills over—liquid down my cheeks as the languish in my chest subsides, just enough. I release my grip on this baby who is God's Son first—indeed, his only Son. Because this is a fact I must never forget, though I fight it more often than I care to admit.

So today, on this day, I find the courage to sing the verse—the one that follows the other two, those words that sort of swaddle all the truth of my firstborn's coming, wrap it up as the gift it is.

Yes, this Gift to the world.

As I hold the side of the cradle, fingers soft around its smoothed-out edges, sanded by good Joseph's hands, I sing—

> O spotless Lamb, my precious Boy,
> You've come to save the world.
> Please start with me, your little mom;
> My heart to you's unfurled.

And having mustered the strength to sing these words, this final verse, my soul feels at peace. I bask for a moment in the light of Jesus's joy before turning to tend to other duties that await, like baking bread to offer life to Joseph, who is busy in his shop—shaping wood, giving it form.

Before I leave his little room, I bend low to kiss my baby on his brow. Jesus smiles sweetly, his eyes closed. And I wonder. Perhaps he's dreaming of the day when he, too, will skip and frolic as all boys do. He'll suffer his share of bumps and bruises, no doubt. But on this, I'm choosing not to dwell—at least for today. Instead, I watch as my lamb sleeps, seemingly in heaven's peace, for now.

And that—yes, this grace—is enough.

> *At day's end, he sleeps*
> *Infant Word who spoke the world*
> *Into form from void.*

"For this is how God loved the world: He gave his one and only Son, so that everyone who believes in him will not perish but have eternal life." (John 3:16)

Touched You Last

Michelle Rayburn

F A GRANDMA TRAINING SCHOOL existed, surely Grandma Ruby would have graduated at the top of her class. I'm certain she aced her way through Playdough and Water Messes 101, and she had extra credit in Hugs, Kisses, and Warm Fuzzies. She could have taught Blanket Forts 201. If being a grandmother ever frustrated her, she never let on.

Now that I'm a grandmother to four, I wonder how she managed to mask any possible sign of irritation when we all descended on her home for holidays. A half-dozen pairs of little feet clomped up and down her stairs all afternoon—from the porch-turned-playroom to the upstairs guestroom, then back to the playroom, then upstairs to drag out the old bridesmaid dresses and hats—and Grandma kept smiling and supplying bottles and boxes for our pretend grocery store and pennies for the cash register.

We pumped the antique organ in the bedroom above the living room for hours, but Grandma never complained of a headache. Perhaps the empty bottles of aspirin and Excedrin she supplied for our play store told a secret we were too young to grasp. And now that I think of it, maybe that's why she often gave us each a quarter and let the whole pack of us walk over to Ben Franklin to buy a special treat. "Be careful when you cross the street" was our only instruction.

While Mom and the aunties bumped hips with Grandma in the small kitchen, peeling potatoes and stirring gravy, Dad and the uncles caught up in the living room on Grandpa's stories of so-and-so's farm and the effects of last summer's drought.

Soon, the summons came to gather in the dining room, adults at the big oak pedestal table, kids at the folding card table. Bowed heads as Grandpa said the prayer. A flurry of conversation and clanking of dishes as heaping bowls and platters passed around the circle and over to our table of squirrely cousins. Dinner rolls, dinner conversation, laughter, and then silence when Grandpa reached under the table to the nook between the pedestal and sliders to retrieve the Bible kept there. I'll never forget his low, monotone way of reading Scripture after every meal, even holidays, and the slight lilt present in his number "tdee," a blend of the English three and Dutch *drie*.

I never cared about the mashed potatoes, squash, corn, or ham. Not the Jell-O "salad." Not even the Christmas pies. I waited for the snack trays Grandma set out after we opened gifts. This was no ordinary spread. Tupperware container after container full of treats. And she had a stacking Regal Ware picnic set of aluminum trays that clamped together with layer upon layer of different goodies. To my childhood mind, it looked just like the tower of communion trays that only adults could touch at church—only these were filled with holiday surprises.

Whether or not my appetite had returned, there was always room for the chocolate-dipped confections, popcorn, nuts, bars, or shortbread cookies. And Grandma Ruby's goodies included treats from the *store* that we never got at any other time of the year. Butter pecan snowball cookies. Cherry almond cookies that melted in my mouth. Windmill cookies for our Dutch traditions. And long before Cherry Coke was a thing, Grandma's Christmas snack buffet included cherry Kool-Aid mixed with RC Cola served in her fanciest ruby-red juice tumblers.

We lived across town, and on occasion, the cousins all stayed overnight, and the moms and dads went home. Grandma often allowed us to set up elaborate tents constructed with folding tables and blankets in the living room. She'd crawl inside with a flashlight and share an imaginary feast with us or bring little plastic oleo bowls of Froot Loops for a bedtime snack. She didn't make us take the tents down at night, as we had to do at home. Instead, she let us sleep in them. *And* leave them up the next day. I always figured being a grandma held a certain kind of magic that made those sorts of messes not as annoying as they were for mothers.

I used to giggle when Grandma Ruby came to tuck us in. She'd put on her housecoat and slippers, put her teeth in the cup by the bathroom sink, and then come kiss us with soft, puckered lips. I liked the way she sounded without her teeth. She sort of smacked when she spoke with her lips folded inward, and words with the letter *S* made a whistling sound.

> Grandma Ruby's house was always the kind of haven that no grandchild ever wanted to leave.

Grandma Ruby's house was always the kind of haven that no grandchild ever wanted to leave. When I was young, she tried to soften the send-off with a baggie of sweets—pink wafer cookies, peppermints, pink and white frosted animal cookies, or bright lollipops with gooey chocolate centers that kept us occupied on the way home. I'm seeing the theme here now that I put it on paper. Grandma was all about goodies! And full disclosure: she didn't stop the takeout treats when we got older.

WHEN I WAS TEN, OUR family moved two hours away from Grandma and Grandpa's house. Saying goodbye was even harder when we knew it would be longer between visits. I can't remember exactly how it started, but we made up a little game. Before we hopped in the Volkswagen for the trip home, I would touch Grandma on the shoulder and say, "Touched you last," and then run away and race to get my car door slammed. Sometimes, she could catch me before I got to the car. Other times, she reached in Dad's door, stretching her arm to the back seat, and touched me last just before we drove away.

For more than three decades, we kept up the tradition at every Christmas and holiday, chasing each other and getting the last touch when our visit ended. In her nineties, Grandma Ruby's mobility changed, and she started using her cane not only for walking but for a last-touch advantage. Running was one of the things she always said she "yusta-could" do. So instead of running, she poked her cane around or between the cluster of hugging loved ones, made contact with an elbow or thigh, and declared victory. I learned to use the excuse of one more stop at the restroom as a means of sneaking back inside for a surprise win.

When my little boys continued the next generation of the game with Great-Grandma Ruby, it put a sparkle in her eye, and I let her win more often. I never minded because kissing her velvety, wrinkled cheek was worth losing the game. "Touched you last," she'd whisper in my ear as I sank into her pillowy shoulder. We continued it when she moved out of the farmhouse to a smaller ranch just blocks away and eventually the nursing home. And then, at last, the game ended when I placed my hand on her wooden casket and said, "I touched you last."

But did I really?

As clans grow, extended family gatherings have a way of becoming more infrequent. My husband and I eventually moved even farther away. Cousins' families grew and spread out too. The blanket forts, pretend play, and pump organ days have long ago faded into memories instead of traditions.

My parents are now the great-grandparents, and I'm the grandma. All of my grandparents have passed on. But at Christmas and throughout the year, the lessons of love, faith, and hope from those long departed are always present. Our loved ones have not left us. They're in our DNA. They're in the smiles around the table. In the faith legacy represented in the nativity story we read before opening presents and in the songs we sing on Christmas Eve as we hold candles and join hands. They are always in our hearts.

In reality, Grandma Ruby touched me last. And now, it's my turn.

Final Thoughts

Michelle Rayburn

BELIEVE THIS IS THE PART of the book where we light tiny candles, and I lead in the opening notes of a hushed "Silent Night" followed by "O Little Town of Bethlehem." We finish with a robust rendition of "Joy to the World," trying to keep the wax from flowing like molten lava over our fingers. Then we blow out the candles, hug our dear friends, and wish one another the merriest of Christmases before heading out in the snow.

So, here are a few hugs.

I'm deeply grateful to the twenty-six writers who shared their talents and treasured memories in this book. They brought their best, and we were blessed. If you have enjoyed their stories, please connect with them and find their other books, podcasts, and more.

Special thanks to Sally Ferguson for volunteering when I needed a proofreader for my chapters. Because I can spot anyone else's mistakes but not my own!

Thank you, reader, for joining our Christmas festivities. You are why we keep writing. So here's a big squeeze of gratitude to you.

Jesus, thank you for the humble miracle of your birth. You brought glorious light into the world and eternal hope to our hearts.

We've shared our stories. As we part, let's remember the most important story of all.

Merry Christmas!

Luke 2:1-20

At that time the Roman emperor, Augustus, decreed that a census should be taken throughout the Roman Empire. (This was the first census taken when Quirinius was governor of Syria.) All returned to their own ancestral towns to register for this census. And because Joseph was a descendant of King David, he had to go to Bethlehem in Judea, David's ancient home. He traveled there from the village of Nazareth in Galilee. He took with him Mary, to whom he was engaged, who was now expecting a child.

And while they were there, the time came for her baby to be born. She gave birth to her firstborn son. She wrapped him snugly in strips of cloth and laid him in a manger, because there was no lodging available for them.

That night there were shepherds staying in the fields nearby, guarding their flocks of sheep. Suddenly, an angel of the Lord appeared among them, and the radiance of the Lord's glory surrounded them. They were terrified, but the angel reassured them. "Don't be afraid!" he said. "I bring you good news that will bring great joy to all people. The Savior—yes, the Messiah, the Lord—has been born today in Bethlehem, the city of David! And you will recognize him by this sign: You will find a baby wrapped snugly in strips of cloth, lying in a manger."

Suddenly, the angel was joined by a vast host of others— the armies of heaven—praising God and saying,

> "Glory to God in highest heaven,
> and peace on earth to those with whom God is pleased."

When the angels had returned to heaven, the shepherds

said to each other, "Let's go to Bethlehem! Let's see this thing that has happened, which the Lord has told us about."

They hurried to the village and found Mary and Joseph. And there was the baby, lying in the manger. After seeing him, the shepherds told everyone what had happened and what the angel had said to them about this child. All who heard the shepherds' story were astonished, but Mary kept all these things in her heart and thought about them often. The shepherds went back to their flocks, glorifying and praising God for all they had heard and seen. It was just as the angel had told them.

NOTES

1   Olivia B. Waxman, "The Surprising Reasons Why Gingerbread Men Became a Holiday Classic," TIME, December 22, 2016, https://time.com/4602913/gingerbread-men-history/.

     L.V. Anderson, "Why Do We Shape Gingerbread Cookies Like People?," SLATE, December 24, 2013, https://slate.com/culture/2013/12/gingerbread-man-history-from-frederick-iii-to-elizabeth-i-to-l-frank-baum-to-shrek.html

2   A shorter version of this chapter appeared in: Kathy Carlton Willis, *The Grin Gal's Guide to Joy* (3G Books, 2020).

3   A different version of this story first appeared in: Yvonne Lehman, *Christmas Moments* (Broken Arrow, OK: Grace Publishing, 2014).

4   A previous version of this poem by Pam Farrel appeared in: Marcia Ramsland, *Simplify Your Holidays* (Nashville: Thomas Nelson, 2008).

5   Dr. Seuss, *How the Grinch Stole Christmas!* (New York: Random House, 1957).

6   Another version of this story appeared in: Pam Whitley Taylor, *God's Grace Keeps Pace* (Tustin, CA: Trilogy Christian Publishing, 2022).

7   Author unknown, "Away in a Manger" (public domain).

8   "Away in a Manger."

9   "Away in a Manger."

10   Luke 2:11–12

Meet the Authors

ROSEMARIE DICRISTO has broken many Christmas ornaments over the years, but never any as special as the angel in her story. She's published over one hundred short stories in various magazines and online forums, most recently flash fiction for *Havok* and for two anthologies published by Ye Olde Dragon books. She dedicates her story to the precious memories of her mom and dad.

PAM FARREL and her husband, Bill, are the Co-Directors of Love-Wise Ministry, authors of fifty-nine books, including bestselling *Men Are Like Waffles, Women Are Like Spaghetti*. The Farrels enjoy time with their three sons, three daughters-in-law, and seven grandchildren. They make their home on a liveaboard boat docked in Southern California, so their Christmas card reads, "Seas and Greetings." www.Love-Wise.com

SALLY FERGUSON lives in Jamestown, New York, with her husband, her dad, and a partridge in a pear tree. Actually, it's a bluebird in the backyard, but this is a Christmas book. Together, they are looking for a song for Christmas that will tickle everyone's fancy! Catch up with her at sallyferguson.net and watch for her upcoming Bible study for caregivers.

PAM FIELDS is the wife of Andrew, mother of nine, and grandmother of four. She's always had a heart for encouraging moms in their walk with the Lord and in their mothering journey. She enjoys sharing testimonies on her podcast, *The Mom Next Door: Stories of Faith*. When Pam has some free time, you can find her at coffee with friends or planning her next family gathering at their home in Cookeville, Tennessee. www. TendingFields.net

PAM HALTER is an award-winning children's picture book, middle grade, and YA fantasy author. She is also a freelance editor of picture books. When she's not writing, Pam enjoys quilting, gardening, cooking, reading, playing the piano, Bible study, and doing fun things with her two grands. Pam lives in southern New Jersey with her husband, special needs adult daughter, and four cats. You can learn more about her at www.pamhalter.com.

DELORES CHRISTIAN LIESNER'S passion is to be a noticer—ministering to abuse survivors, caregivers for difficult personalities, parents who've lost a child—and to be the miracle for others. Over a thousand of her stories, devotionals, lessons, and articles are published in print and online, including thirty-one stories and life-changing challenges in her devotional, *Be the Miracle* (Elk Lake Publishing). www.deloresliesner.com

SANDY LIPSKY tries to sit still and compose the things God whispers in her ear. During the day, she writes, teaches piano, and cares for her household. Nighttime, she can be found reading. Sandy is a contributing author for two WordGirls Collective devotional books and has essays in the WordGirls compilations *Live & Learn* and *Sage, Salt & Sunshine*. She enjoys Georgia's seasons and spending time with her husband, daughter, and new puppies Maple and Janie. www.sandylipsky.com

CHARLAINE MARTIN loves helping others discover how God takes us on adventures with him every day. She enjoys cycling on bike trails, swimming in the Florida sunshine, flying with her Boaz, and sharing tickle bugs with their grandchildren. She is a writer and contributing author in *Wit, Wisdom & Whimsy*, *Snapshots of Hope & Heart*, and *Live & Learn*. You can find her at www.charlainemartin.com.

BECKY MELBY has been married to her high school sweetheart for fifty-one years. They are the proud parents of four sons who have blessed them with four beautiful daughters-in-love and fifteen grandchildren. Becky has authored and co-authored twenty-seven inspirational novels and novellas and one nonfiction book, *Spouse in the House*. For more information, find her at www.beckymelby.com or on Facebook.

MAUREEN MILLER is an award-winning author who writes for *Guideposts* and her local newspaper. She's written for several online devotional websites and numerous collaboratives as well and enjoys life with her husband and their three "born in their hearts" children and grandchildren on Selah Farm, their hobby homestead in North Carolina. She blogs at www.penningpansies.com, sharing God's extraordinary character in the ordinary things of life, and she's finishing her first novel with Redemption Press.

KELLY WILSON MIZE is a wife, mother of two young adults, cat mom, and former educator with a master's degree in education. In twenty years as a published author, she has composed numerous articles, interviews, curriculum projects, and devotions—including contributions to nine traditionally published books. Credits include Lifeway, Bethany House, Guideposts, (in)courage, and others. Kelly's first picture book, *The Beautiful Story Within Me*, was published in 2021. Visit Kelly's website at www.kellywilsonmize.com.

ROBYN MULDER lives in South Dakota with her husband, Gary. She is a writer and freelance editor who loves languages, traveling, music, and crafting. She and her husband have four adult children and two adorable grandchildren, all of whom live conveniently in Lincoln, Nebraska. Robyn writes about mental health, faith, and perseverance at www.robynmulder.com and is the host of the podcast *Catch Your Thoughts with Robyn Mulder.*

KRISTINE ZIMMER ORKIN's tagline "Finding blessings in life's burdens" reflects her core belief that life's seasons are paired with purpose and blessings. Kris writes inspirational nonfiction stories. She is published in several anthologies, magazines, and blogs in the United States and UK. Her book *Widow Unprepared* is an upfront memoir of widowhood and single parenting after her husband's 2007 sudden death. Son Jacob ("Jakey") was stillborn in 1987. Connect with Kris at kporkin2954@gmail.com.

Sharing the gospel through writing and speaking is one of **BETTY PREDMORE's** favorite things to do. She engages her audiences with her easy, conversational style. Her words make women pause and ponder the possibilities of a beautiful life with Christ. As an author, Christian communicator, and ministry leader, Betty uses every opportunity to encourage women to live their best life in Christ, overcoming the strongholds that hold them captive. You can visit Betty at www.momsenseinc.org.

MARY ANNE QUINN lives in Chicago. She and her husband, John, enjoy relaxing on Lake Michigan's beaches, birdwatching in local forest preserves, and putting together jigsaw puzzles. She's on her own singing in an annual Handel's Messiah concert. Mary Anne's stories are characterized by whimsy, humor, and faith in the goodness of God. Her creativelyattached.com ministry helps people experience emotional healing, as well as build joy and resiliency in the living, interactive presence of Jesus.

MICHELLE RAYBURN is the managing editor for this project and a publisher who enjoys collaborating with others to create heartwarming collections. She also loves working with other authors and indie publishers as an editor, graphic designer, and typesetter. An author and podcast host (*Life Repurposed* podcast) who helps others find hope in the trashy stuff of life, Michelle has an MA in ministry leadership and writes Christian living books, humor, and Bible studies. Together with her husband, they've raised two sons and gained two daughters-in-law—plus three granddaughters and a grandson. Dark chocolate, an iced coffee, and a good book in the hammock top Michelle's favorites list. www.michellerayburn.com

JOANIE SHAWHAN shares true-life stories, offering her reader an eyewitness view of the action. Her Selah Awards finalist book *In Her Shoes: Dancing in the Shadow of Cancer* reflects the value of "Your story plus my story become our stories." An ovarian cancer survivor and registered nurse, Joanie speaks to medical students in the Survivors Teaching Students program. She co-founded an ovarian cancer social group: The Fried Eggs—Sunny-Side Up. Follow Joanie at www.joanieshawhan.com.

Author and speaker **HEATHER NORMAN SMITH** has published five novels set in her home state of North Carolina and has also written or contributed to multiple nonfiction compilations. Her goal in writing is to entertain and encourage while illuminating the redemptive love of God. Heather is married and has four very active children. Along with writing, speaking, and spending time with her family, she also enjoys singing about Jesus. Learn more at www.heathernormansmith.com.

BARBARA SYVERTSON writes about experiences where she sees God in the unusual situations of life. She and her husband, Ed, live in Pennsylvania, where they enjoy small-town living and spending time with their eight grandchildren. Their home is often filled with toys, chaos, take-out food, and joy. She was a contributing author to *Heart Renovation* by Katy Kauffman.

MEL TAVARES is a New Englander who loves to cook for and host her large multi-cultural family. If you can't find her in the kitchen, check her writing studio. She is an award-winning author, speaker, and life coach. www.drmeltavares.com

PAM WHITLEY TAYLOR is a wife, mother, and grandmother. She served as the primary caregiver for sixteen years to her multi-handicapped daughter and oversaw her care for another twelve years. She was a speaker for Christian Women's Club for fifteen years. Today, she enjoys writing, photographing the critters that visit her yard daily, and RVing with her husband, John. She is the author of *God's Grace Keeps Pace*.

JONI TOPPER loves to sing. After a thirty-year career at the post office, she started writing and discovered another passion. Since 2022, her stories have appeared in *Guideposts*, *Now What?*, *Breakthrough Intercessors*, and book collaborations *Sage, Salt & Sunshine* and *Life in the Estrogen-Free Zone*. Joni speaks and leads worship for women's events. Supporting the interests of five grandchildren keeps her and her husband of forty-two years young at heart. Learn more at www.morningloryministry.com.

GAYLE VEITENHEIMER writes inspirational stories and creative nonfiction that encourage children to walk out their Christian faith. She holds a Master of Arts in Biblical Studies from Dallas Theological Seminary. Her website and blog can be found at gayleveitenheimer.com, where she challenges parents and families to follow hard after God through healthy doses of practical application.

HEIDI VERTREES, author/educator, manages www.newsongpress.net with Christian tips for teaching children and teens writing. She authored *Victor Survives Being a Kid*, a multi-award-winning book for middle graders, available on Amazon and other online retailers. This humorous, action/adventure fiction is told by a fifth grader. Heidi Vertrees has enjoyed many years of teaching. She and her husband live in Maryland, where she teaches swimming to homeschool students and leads a CEF Bible club for children.

HALLY J. WELLS is a Christian speaker, freelance writer, and former school counselor. Inspired by people and personalities, Hally writes about faith, parenting, and mental illness. Hally's biological, adopted, step, and foster kids, along with many students, have both awed and exhausted her. Hally offers practical answers, resources, faith-family support, and divine wisdom to overwhelmed parents—digging deep enough to find the good stuff, reaching high enough to find the best! Visit Hally at www.hallyjwells.com.

KATHY CARLTON WILLIS, God's Grin Gal, writes and speaks with a balance of funny and faith, whimsy and wisdom. She coaches others to remove the training wheels of doubt and not just risk but also take pleasure in the joy ride of life. She is known for her debut book, *Grin with Grace*, and for her grinning Boston terrier, Hettie. www.kathycarltonwillis.com

LISA-ANNE WOOLDRIDGE is inspired by illuminated manuscripts and stained-glass windows. Her heartwarming true stories have been published in several popular collections. Her second novel, The Cozy Cat Bookstore Mysteries—*The Rose and Crown*, is now available online. She lives in the land of mountains and valleys that drink in the rain of heaven—otherwise known as Oregon, or you may find her at www.Lisa-Anne.net.

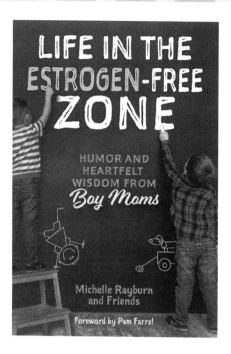

If you enjoyed this book, check out other compilations by Michelle Rayburn and friends.